IMAGES OF FIRE

This book is dedicated
to all the many fire-fighters
who over the years have laid down their lives
in the pursuance of their noble profession

*Aftermath of the Kings Cross
Underground tragedy. Some time
after the intense fire that swept
up an escalator and into the
crowded booking hall has been
put out, fire officers in breathing
apparatus prepare to enter the
doomed booking hall. Note the high
degree of smoke damage at
ceiling level. Thirty passengers
and a fire officer died.
18 November 1987* (London Fire
Brigade)

IMAGES OF FIRE

150 Years of Fire-fighting

Neil Wallington

DAVID & CHARLES
Newton Abbot   London

ACKNOWLEDGEMENTS

The undertaking of such a work as *Images of Fire* would simply not have been possible without the assistance I have so readily received from many colleagues serving throughout the British Fire Service. I am indebted to them all for their support and co-operation. I also wish to thank the staff of the libraries of the Fire Service College, the Fire Protection Association, and the London Fire Brigade for their unstinting assistance during my research.

Mrs Gertrude Young of Honiton typed the manuscript with great diligence and care, and gave valuable advice for which I am grateful. My children have also been very tolerant of their father whilst this book has been in preparation and, once again, I have received the most enormous encouragement from my dear wife Sue throughout the various gestation stages of this work.

Lastly, I have to point out that any views which I have expressed in these pages are simply my own personal beliefs and opinions on a noble profession that I hold very dear.

Neil Wallington
Woodbury,
Exeter,
Devon.

Wallington, Neil
  Images of fire
  1. Great Britain. Fire-fighting
  history
  I. Title.
  628.9′25.′0941

ISBN 0-7153-9340-5

© Neil Wallington, 1989

Printed in Portugal
by Resopal
for David & Charles Publishers plc
Brunel House   Newton Abbot   Devon

By the same Author:
Fireman! A Personal Account
Firemen at War
'999' – The Accident and Crash Rescue
Work of the Fire Service

CONTENTS

FOREWORD

Throughout history fire has been both a friend and an enemy of man, and when used as a weapon of war it is as deadly in this modern age as it was way back in history. Surprisingly, in today's society we appear to be more than ever vulnerable to the possibility of involvement in fire accidents, and often the effect on people of such involvement is horrifying in terms of pain and disfigurement. Incidents of both past and present tend to indicate the vulnerability of our cities, industries, transport systems, forestry and agriculture to devastation by fire damage. Modern technology and development of our now considerably automated society indicate no sign of solving the problem.

Reaction to accidents and other requirements such as wartime measures have been responsible for considerable investment and effort to develop and expand fire-fighting and rescue organisations capable of meeting the new threat and protecting public interests. The massive aerial bombing attacks on cities during the early 1940 period presented a requirement for nationwide reinforcement arrangements and standardisation of fire-fighting equipment. The post World War II development of our cities with highrise buildings, massive shopping complexes, environmental schemes and dense traffic conditions today present the fire and rescue services with many new and complex problems. Coupled with these has been the emergence of enormous bulk carrier shipping, passenger aircraft and crowded motorway road systems all tending to increase the size, scale and complexity of fires and accidents.

Modern technology also presents substantial problems, as epitomised by the recent nuclear accident at Chernobyl. There, radio-activity proved fatal to the fire-fighting crews and spread danger over a considerable area of population. The Bradford football stadium disaster, the King's Cross underground fire, and the Boeing 737 crash on the M1, all involving multiple deaths of the public, clearly illustrate the problems facing the present-day emergency services. A number of recent serious fire and explosion accidents have also occurred, involving off-shore oil installations with considerable loss of life.

Neil Wallington, the author of this book, has outstanding experience in the field of fire-fighting and emergency rescue organisation, and their development. He commands the very large and complex Devon Fire and Rescue Service, and has considerable operational working experience in the Greater London area and other areas of the country. He is the author of several interesting accounts of the work of our emergency services.

I commend this new publication which should suitably supplement those earlier books and provide a fascinating, graphic yet sombre reminder of the dangers of fire, and the selfless service given to the community by fire-fighters both ancient and modern.

Sir Peter Darby, CBE, C St J, QFSM, FIFireE, CBIM
Chief Fire Officer London Fire Brigade, 1977–81
HM Chief Inspector of Fire Services England and Wales,
1981–87

Firemen undergoing breathing apparatus training under controlled conditions inside a purpose-built firehouse at the Devon Fire and Rescue Service's Plymouth Training School. The men are about to extinguish the small crib fire. Superheated steam will then envelop them to add to the already high temperature and smoke levels (Devon Fire and Rescue Service)

INTRODUCTION

It is probably true that today the fire service enjoys more media coverage of its activities than at any other period in its history. Indeed, there are times when it seems that dramatic images of firemen at work are hardly ever missing from television news screens or the pages of national or local newspapers. In recent times there has been the particular death and devastation caused by fire at Bradford City football club. Here, in a short few minutes in 1985, a carelessly discarded cigarette end amid an accumulation of rubbish under the main stand led to such awful television sights as people actually on fire as they attempted to escape from the spreading inferno. Since then, in November 1987, London fire-fighters found themselves facing a major incident at King's Cross underground station towards the end of the evening rush hour. Once again, mass media coverage brought into millions of homes across the United Kingdom the overall scene of swirling smoke and the shock felt by all those hundreds of casualties caught up in the mêlée.

But at King's Cross no camera could ever record the real battle fought by firemen where rescue and fire-fighting operations were being carried out below ground. Here, in searing heat and high humidity, fire crews took the most awful physical punishment. Many of the initial rescue teams had to descend stairs into the inferno, passing through a veritable chimney-flue effect of super-heated smoke and gases travelling upwards from the fire below.

The later television scenes of blackened, sweating and exhausted firemen sitting on kerb edges told their own story. The men's faces showed clearly the horrors they had faced, and also revealed that they knew that Station Officer Colin Townsley, the first supervisory officer to arrive at the scene, had died during a gallant personal rescue attempt in the early stages of the fire. Their faces were images of men who had once again, as firemen, looked death squarely in the face.

Recently, during New Year 1988, there were even more particularly poignant images of fire, as crews of Mid Glamorgan Fire Service in south Wales cleared up and damped down the smoke-blackened house at Merthyr Tydfil in which almost a whole family – a father and four young children – perished, despite heroic rescue attempts by firemen. Here, once again, the killer was smoke, exacerbated by polyurethane-filled furniture which, once involved in even a small fire, quickly produces vast volumes of thick, toxic black smoke

The nature of the beast. A huge fireball erupts over Laporte's Chemical Works, Warrington, Cheshire, during a large fire in 1985 which involved a hundred fire-fighters (Warrington Guardian)

sufficient to fill an average house in about two minutes, and to suffocate all therein. This fire, and several other fatal blazes over the New Year holiday, resulted in great strides being taken by government to begin to outlaw combustible foam fillings in furniture. Prior to this there had been very considerable lobbying from the country's principal fire officers, whose firemen in recent times have had to attend an ever-increasing number of fatal fires involving polyurethane foam in dwellings.

Such fire-service media attention has, however, not always taken place and the steadily increasing coverage has only come about over the past two decades or so. Before then, firemen really did operate in what was a virtual 'silent service' – a profession whose working practices were not projected at all to the outside world. But by the late 1960s, and in the face of spiralling public deaths and injuries from fire and soaring financial fire-loss figures, firemen were beginning to mount effective public safety campaigns. And in so doing, fire-fighters began to tell a little of their world of sudden drama as a '999' fire call was received, the big red fire station doors crashed open and several red fire-engines headed off noisily and speedily to the scene of the emergency.

But a fireman's life today is not all dashing to fires. In fact, he spends a very small percentage of his on-duty time dealing with '999' emergencies. The bulk of his time is spent in training himself and preparing his great quantity of equipment for that sudden and unrelenting moment when a life will depend on a fireman's skill, resourcefulness and selfless courage. Today's fire-fighter is a veritable jack-of-all trades technocrat. He has to have a good understanding of such subjects as building construction, electricity, chemistry and combustion, and mechanical engineering. A basic knowledge of psychology and medicine is also necessary, as is hydraulics – the fireman's art of moving water rapidly from one place to another.

A fireman also has to be extremely fit to work in basements and at great heights, frequently in cramped and claustrophobic situations. He must have a self-discipline second to none as he dons his life-support set (his breathing apparatus) and heads into a building from which everyone else is fleeing. He must be able to work in great heat and extreme conditions of humidity, in winter and in summer. In addition, at times he must steel himself to deal with the aftermath of human carelessness, error or accident which may result in human tragedy and suffering of a wide and extreme nature. So often when someone dies an unnecessary death in a fire or in a car crash during the early hours of a morning, the chances are that it will not be a priest who administers the last rites but a fireman.

There are today in the United Kingdom sixty-seven public fire brigades, usually based upon the county areas

The Kings Cross fire: scene showing the aftermath of the tragedy at the top of the Piccadilly Line escalator where many of the fatalities occured. 18 November 1987 (London Fire Brigade)

The Kings Cross tragedy, with a view of severe fire damage looking up to the top of the ill-fated Piccadilly Line escalator. 18 November 1987 (London Fire Brigade)

11

or the larger metropolitan cities. These brigades are manned by about 42,300 professional full-time fire-fighters, backed up in the more rural areas by around 19,000 retained or volunteer firemen. This latter group undertakes to provide an immediate response to a 'bleeper' call from the brigade's central control room, where all '999' emergency calls are handled. Retained personnel have to be able to leave their daytime job or be on call from their homes during the dark hours — community service of the first order in those geographical parts of the United Kingdom where the risk of fire is fairly low and a professional full-time presence could not be justified.

The largest brigade today is that of London, with 114 fire stations manned full-time by around 6,900 officers, men and women. At the other end of the scale is the Isle of Wight Fire and Rescue Service with 11 fire stations crewed by 49 full-time and 158 volunteers.

The total number of '999' emergency calls dealt with by all United Kingdom brigades is a staggering figure which, in general terms, has continued to rise very steadily over the 150 years of organised fire brigades. Apart from fires, over the past 30 years there has also been a dramatic rise in 'special service' calls, such as road and rail crashes, chemical leakages, machinery accidents, and children and animals trapped or caught up in all sorts of predicaments.

The following figures give some idea of the growth of firemen's operational work. Despite great efforts by fire brigades through both fire safety laws and goodwill advice aimed at minimising the deaths, injury and huge property losses which occur almost unstoppably each successive year, these statistics make depressing reading. In 1967 for instance, firemen in England and Wales responded to about 387,000 emergency calls. By 1987, this total had almost doubled to some 728,000 individual '999' calls for help. During 1987, there were in England and Wales 750 fire deaths, over 142,000 fires in property and seven firemen lost their lives whilst in operational action. The trends in Scotland show the same patterns.

Today's fire brigades are the nation's premier emergency and rescue organisation, ready to tackle any situation at a moment's notice. Horrific fires such as at Bradford City football club in 1985 and at King's Cross underground station in 1987 are only the public face of a fireman's job, as are the frequent motorway accidents of the highway age. More recently has come Lockerbie, the Clapham Junction rail crash and the M1 aircraft disaster. The fire service has a proud and historic past which has in a sense imbued the modern fire-fighter with a spirit of adventure essential in every recruit to a profession where personal danger is never far away. Such a spirit can probably be traced to the very origins of fire-fighting, as the following chapter will show.

1 A NOBLE PROFESSION IS BORN

For fire to occur, there must be present three factors: fuel, a source of ignition and oxygen. Fire therefore has been a permanent threat to life and property ever since man first learnt to kindle a flame. Consequently it is not surprising to discover that the first attempts at fire-fighting go back to the second century BC, when an Alexandrian named Ctesibus invented a hand pump that could throw a jet of water onto a fire. This pump had two cylinders with valves to admit water and then to expel it under pressure. Parts of such very early fire pumps have been found in the United Kingdom at Silchester, as well as in Italy.

However, it really was the Roman Empire that provided some of the first positive community fire protection for, although mechanical pumps were still rare, the Romans concentrated on organised manpower to form the core of their fire defence. With slave labour abounding, suitable men were readily available to be located at strategic points around the cities, to provide an early warning of fire. Unfortunately, records show that many slaves were – not surprisingly – unreliable, and in AD6, one quarter of the entire centre of Rome was destroyed in one devastating conflagration.

This catastrophe brought about major improvements in Roman fire protection, with the formation of a corps of fire-fighters known as *vigiles*, whose members enjoyed a high social status and collective style of living in barracks, each with its own baths. The *vigiles* were formed into three basic groups whose fire-fighting functions were:

1 as providers of water to the fire via organised double-line bucket-chains; one line passed water to the blaze, the other returned the buckets for re-filling.
2 as crews who actually operated the fire pump.
3 *Vigiles* whose primary task was to pull down those parts of walls and roofs that were burning, to provide a fire-break and thus to restrict the rapid spread of the fire through starving it of ready material upon which to feed. These latter crews were armed with ladders and long hooks to provide the necessary reach. They must have been extremely courageous to carry out their critical work close to and underneath dangerous fire situations with, one suspects, little personal protection.

VALUE FOR MONEY VIGILES

During Roman times, the *Vigiles* who formed the corps of professional fire-fighters also carried out other responsibilities. These supplementary duties included early fire prevention in which they had a right of entry into any premises to check on the safe use of fire, for cooking, heating or lighting.

However, it is believed that the *Vigiles* were expected also to chase escaping slaves. Another rather odd duty for a fire-fighter was to guard the garments of bathers taking their daily dip in the municipal bath.

The Romans went on to establish various corps of *vigiles* in Britain through the import of fire-fighting skills and experience gained in Rome. Unfortunately, as the Roman Empire declined, so too did all the fire-protection progress of those times and any awareness of the dangers of fire over the next few centuries seems poorly recorded.

There is documentation showing great devastation by fire at Canterbury in 624, and London suffered huge fires in 798 and 982. The major problem was that most properties were of timber construction with thatched roofs, and therefore easily combustible. Most early chimney flues were constructed of hollowed-out tree-trunks, while many domestic fires for heating and cooking were simply lit in the centre of a room. Smoke and sparks were carried upwards on convection currents, to find their way out to the open air by way of a hole in the roof. In 989 there was one of the largest fires yet to afflict the capital. It was, as chronicles relate, 'so great and lamentable a fire that, beginning in Aldgate, it burned down houses and churches all the way to Ludgate together with the stately Fabrick of St Paul's'.

Soon after the Norman invasion there came a law requiring fires and lights to be extinguished at nightfall. A metal fire-cover was used for this purpose, and from the French *couvre feu* came the modern term 'curfew'.

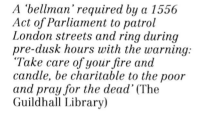

A 'bellman' required by a 1556 Act of Parliament to patrol London streets and ring during pre-dusk hours with the warning: 'Take care of your fire and candle, be charitable to the poor and pray for the dead' (The Guildhall Library)

But this attempt at fire safety was unpopular and was abolished in 1100. This was quite remarkable, as major fires continued to occur, causing multiple deaths and massive damage.

Fire-fighting equipment of those times was still largely restricted to the bucket-chains, ladders and long drag-hooks of Roman times. Progress on machine-powered water jets was virtually at a standstill. However, forward-thinking was taking place. In 1189 the first Lord Mayor of London, Henry Fitzalwin, issued a local law to require all new buildings in the City of London to be built of stone and roofed with slate or clay tiles. For the first time, the owners of large houses were also required to have ready long ladders for escape, and to provide large barrels of water nearby. But this did not prevent the First Great Fire of London from occurring in 1212. It is believed to have started on the wooden London Bridge and it spread to both sides of the capital, causing over 3,000 deaths. Medieval fires had a horrible habit of returning to the same location, and major blazes again struck St Paul's Cathedral, York Minster and the Devon town of Tiverton in successive years of the Middle Ages.

It was the Second Great Fire of London in 1666 which finally provided the impetus to move forward the science of fire-fighting from the basic provisions of the Roman *vigiles* still generally in use in 1666. The Second Great

A print circa 1600 showing typical fire squirts and fire buckets in use (London Fire Brigade)

Abbildung der Statt LONDON, sambt dem erschröcklichen brandt daselten, so 4 tagen lange gewehrt hatt. A: 1666. im 7bris.

1. Yorke house	5. Somerset house.	9. Baynards castl.	13. Guild hall	17. St Petrus
2. Durham house	6. Arundel house.	10. St Andre in Holb	14. St Lorentz Poultney	18. St Duston in the East.
3. New exchange	7. Essex house.	11. St Pauls Church.	15. the Royal exchange	19. Alhallows barking.
4. Savoy	8. Temple.	12. Boo Church	16. St Michael	20. Custom house.

A contemporary print of German origin of the Great Fire of London (London Fire Brigade)

A Hogarth cartoon of the chaos of a 1750 fire scene with the Union Insurance Office firemen suffering some interference and hindrance from firemen of other companies (London Fire Brigade)

Fire started on 2 September 1666 in a baker's shop in Pudding Lane, a narrow street off Eastcheap. The baker, a Mr Farynor, awoke at about 2 am and smelt smoke coming from his shop below. By climbing out of their garret window onto an adjoining roof, he and his family made their escape.

Like many streets in the city, Pudding Lane would hardly allow two hand-carts to pass, and the fire rapidly spread to stocks of hay and fodder on the other side of the lane. One hour later the fire had engulfed most of the buildings nearby, despite strenuous efforts by the large numbers of bucket-chain volunteers who were constantly forced to retreat. By 8 am the fire was spreading in three directions, and was only restricted in the south by the Thames. The fire consumed all in its path, fed by the closeness of properties whose construction had largely ignored the fire-safety requirements as to the ideal spacing of houses with the danger of fire in mind.

The fire burned uncontrolled for four days and nights before many unaffected buildings were demolished in its path to form a huge fire-break. The inferno was thus finally halted late on 5 September. An area of about 1 mile (1.6km) long and ½ mile (.8km) wide was left a charred and smouldering ruin; 13,000 homes, 84 churches, 44 livery halls and many other public buildings were razed to the ground. Over 100,000 people were homeless, but remarkably only 6 people lost their lives. Even then, the cost of the Great Fire was put at £10 million.

THE GREAT FIRE OF LONDON 1666 – A ROYAL CHAIN OF COMMAND

At about 3am, one hour after the initial outbreak of the fire, the Lord Mayor was summoned from his bed to view the rapidly spreading fire. He is reported to have arrived fairly promptly by carriage in the Pudding Lane area, but was quickly dismissive of the situation, saying that it could be easily extinguished if enough persons would urinate upon the blaze. So saying, he promptly returned to his bed.

However, by noon the fire had spread over half-a-mile laterally through riverside warehouses and dwellings, and was growing in intensity by the minute. The Lord Mayor put in another official appearance, this time on horseback. He looked dishevelled and weary as he complained to his aides that no one took any notice of his entreaties to demolish buildings in the path of the fire.

King Charles II had, in fact, already issued orders to the Lord Mayor to pull down property without question wherever a fire-break could be created. But there was chaos everywhere; householders and traders were only anxious to save their belongings and wares, the streets were jammed with the fleeing throng, and looters were also at work in the smoke-filled thoroughfares and alleyways.

Some thirty hours into the fire, the King supplanted the Lord Mayor and vested control of fire-fighting in the Duke of York. Under the Duke's guidance, a number of front-line strategic posts were set up, each manned by several companies of Guards, and 100 men.

But the area of the fire grew inexorably, and later on during day two, the King came in person to witness the clear threat to the capital. He returned on horseback several hours later, and threw coins to the host of volunteer firemen and helpers. At one point, Charles II even joined in a bucket-chain.

By the third night, the Duke of York had drafted large numbers of sailors and dockyard crews to the scene. Gunpowder was used to blow up whole streets and rows of premises, and slowly the weary and toiling fire-fighters began to get the upper hand. The fire was halted soon after midnight on the Thursday morning, and was then slowly extinguished around its perimeter over the next few hours. The huge fire-breaks had done their job.

Metal firemarks of the late eighteenth century were fixed to the external wall of a property to indicate the insurance office whose fire brigade would (hopefully) extinguish any fire. The offices shown are left, Norwich; centre, Sun; and right, Phoenix. Each carry the relevant policy number (London Fire Brigade)

PERKS OF THE JOB

Those recruited to be insurance company firemen not only enjoyed a handsome uniform and generous pay but were also entitled to an exemption from being taken by the press gangs of the Navy. Once a year, insurance company firemen would parade in full uniform through the main streets, and conclude the grand event with a sumptuous dinner.

Of the Second Great Fire was born the first London 'Insurance Office', where cover could be taken out against fire damage. The first was set up in 1680, and many others soon followed. But fire damage was still happening all too frequently, and several of the insurance offices set up their own fire brigades. These consisted of firemen recruited from the many watermen who plied on the Thames. They were employed on a part-time basis and followed their ordinary work until called out to an outbreak of fire by messenger. Insurance firemen wore splendidly decorative and colourful uniforms to indicate their respective company, and they were expected to attend regular drill sessions.

Fire-fighting equipment was now also beginning to be developed and, by the end of the seventeenth century, manually operated pumps were quite commonplace. Some of these were horse drawn. Leather hose was now available, which meant that a jet of water could be taken close to, or even into a burning building, instead of relying on the earlier nozzle fixed to the top of a manual pump. Hand-held fire squirts, like large syringes, were also more readily available although restricted by the need for frequent refills.

Nevertheless, the early days of organised insurance fire brigades were not without difficulty. The various insurance companies marked their insured properties by large metal firemarks or badges placed prominently on a front-facing wall, and thus, early on in a fire, it was

A typical liveried insurance fireman, circa 1832, being of the Royal Exchange *fire office. Note the company arm badge and elaborately tailored uniform, hardly suitable for the rigours of fire-fighting; also the manual fire pump in background* (London Fire Brigade)

clear whose responsibility was the extinction of the blaze. At first, firemen maintained by, say, the Sun Fire Office would deal only with a fire in a property insured with their company. If the Sun firemen arrived first on the scene, to find a house displaying, say, a Westminster firemark, they would literally stand by and watch the fire take hold. Worse still, during the time up to the early 1700s, 'rival' firemen would actively engage in harassing and obstructing their competitors, and many fights broke out against the backdrop of a burning property.

However, after several major London fires had developed whilst such chaos ensued, it became clear that insurance companies had to be more circumspect in such matters. By the early eighteenth century, co-operation became a more regular feature and brigades got straight to work at a fire even though the burning property was not insured with their particular office. Nevertheless, competition and rivalry between brigades remained intense.

Outside of London and the large cities, fire-fighting remained the legal duty of the parish authorities who were obliged to provide a large and a small engine, together with lengths of leather hose. The custodians of the engines were paid rewards according to their order of arrival at a fire.

Thus organised fire-fighting in the United Kingdom moved towards the nineteenth century, and although huge fires still took place causing death, much material damage and disruption to the livelihood of a community, some semblance of order was emerging — even if still slowly — from centuries of inactivity and complacency. The early nineteenth century was to see an absolute revolution in fire-fighting equipment, methods and training; a revolution which was to lead directly to the birth of the modern fire service.

'BEER OH!'

Manual fire engines were extremely hard work for those operating the pump handles either side of the main body of the appliance. Early pumps had relatively short handles which could only be pumped up and down by two or three persons each side. As one group pumped down on one side, the handles on the other came up, and very quickly a strong rhythmic motion could be achieved. Hopefully, providing enough water was being discharged into the well of the pump, either by bucket-chain or later on by leather hose, the actions of the pumpers produced a reasonably high pressure jet from the fixed nozzle on the very top of the appliance itself.

After the Great Fire of 1666, pump manufacturers increased the size of the pump mechanism to pump greater quantities of water at higher pressures. There was, therefore, a need for more leverage on the pumping handles, which became longer and more substantial in construction.

The volunteers who manned the handles usually expected some liquid refreshment during their physical efforts, upon which of course often depended the successful outcome of the fire-fighting. At a very large and protracted fire, these volunteer pumpers would very soon get into their stride, bending their backs in unison on each side of the pump. They soon learnt to call or sing out together to help their coordination and, after a while, to boost their flagging energy and their aching arms and shoulders. A common cry whilst pumping was 'Beer Oh! Beer Oh!' in time with the up-and-down movement of the pump handles. No doubt this was a reminder that the pumpers were expecting some ale — indeed, there are recorded instances of pumping coming to an abrupt halt when it was known that there would be a delay in the arrival of a thirst-quenching barrel or two!

2 TWO FIREMEN OF VISION

James Braidwood

The life of James Braidwood revolved around fire, fire-engines and fire-fighting, and in 1824 at the age of twenty-four he was appointed to the impressive-sounding post of Master of Fire Engines at the Edinburgh Fire Engine Establishment. This brigade had recently been formed following an amalgamation of various insurance brigades protecting the Edinburgh area, and it became the first municipally controlled fire brigade in the country. Braidwood's upbringing under his builder father had given young James a healthy interest in building construction and surveying, but on leaving school he had joined an Edinburgh volunteer fire brigade. From then on his direction had been without doubt.

When he became the chief of the much-enlarged Edinburgh brigade, with its eighty part-time firemen, he was already an acknowledged theorist and practical planner for more effective fire-fighting methods and organisation. Braidwood broke new ground wherever he went, and he put an emphasis on training not experienced previously. Under his command, all fire-fighting crews were regularly turned out of their beds at 4 o'clock in the morning to pitch ladders and provide jets of water in awkward and inaccessible parts of Edinburgh's buildings. The employers of Braidwood's eighty part-time firemen complained bitterly, saying that their workers were being overworked, but Braidwood would have none of it. He pointed to the enthusiasm shown by his fire-fighters who, having trained in the dark hours, could perform all the multiplicity of firemen's tasks with confidence and pride. Indeed, Braidwood boasted that his men could turn out to a fire and, in a little over one minute of arrival at a blaze, could have hoses connected to a manual pump and get a water jet to work off ladders at close range to the fire.

Braidwood was still only thirty when he produced his first technical paper on fire-engine construction, firemen's training and methods of fire-fighting. He was particularly critical of the accepted practice of pumping vast quantities of water onto burning buildings from 'long shot' jets in a haphazard manner. He emphasised the prime need for fire-fighting crews to get into a burning building and to seek the real source of the fire at close range, even though this meant considerable

---

HAZARDS OF THE JOB

Being a fireman, especially in Braidwood's days, always carried the chance of an involuntary soaking. Such wettings were most frequently caused when a manual pump needed to be connected to a basic water supply before a controlled fire-fighting jet could be directed at the fire.

As water mains came to be commonplace, at least on main throughfares, fire plugs were fitted at intervals. These were nothing more than up-right outlets for fire-fighting purposes, and were normally blocked off by a large tapered wooden plug.

When needed, a fireman would simply knock out the plug and then attempt to insert a tapered standpipe and hose connection into the water main against the flow of mains pressure. This task was never achieved without a soaking, and when valved outlets became standard fittings for fire service hydrants from about 1870 onwards, the connection of a pump to mains water became a much less hazardous operation.

physical punishment in heat, smoke and humidity for his men who in those days had no breathing apparatus to protect their own respiratory systems. James Braidwood's eighty Edinburgh part-timers were therefore the first 'smoke-eating' close-range firemen, whose strategies and tactics founded the very basis for modern fire-fighting.

But, on the negative side, it was perhaps Braidwood's insistence on care with water that held him back from venturing more rapidly into a wider use of steam-powered pumps. Such fire-engines were being developed from 1829 onwards, and were made available by John Braithwaite and John Ericsson, both London-based engineers with a great interest in steam and fire-fighting. Braidwood publicly declared that steam-driven water jets would be too powerful, dangerous to firemen and public alike, and could cause additional damage to the fabric of a building. Thus the Edinburgh brigade was committed to manual pumps for years to come.

Braidwood was not only a planner and administrator. At fires, he led his men very much from the front and at one particular major conflagration he personally rescued nine people by dragging them from peril in a smoke-filled house.

Meanwhile, the growing efficiency of the Edinburgh Fire Engine Establishment under Braidwood had not gone unnoticed in London. In the capital during the 1800s there had been a steady growth of insurance company brigades, notably the Sun, the Royal Exchange and the Phoenix. The feverish competition and rivalry of the previous century had long gone, although there were still constant squabbles between various companies over the numbers of firemen made available to respond to fire calls, as well as how best they could work together at incidents. Furthermore, as the capital continued to grow in size and population, the relative number of manual pumps provided by the insurance companies gradually dropped. Fortunately for the citizens of London, such shortcomings could not go on and in 1826 there were clear moves towards more ready co-ordination of each separate brigade and its resources for the benefit of all concerned. This progress led to an agreement in 1832 to bring the majority of insurance brigades under one new umbrella organisation – the London Fire Engine Establishment. Ten separate insurance companies contributed their firemen to the new brigade, which collectively protected about two-thirds of all the property in London.

When consideration was being given to the choice of a leader for the new London brigade, it was perhaps not too surprising that eyes were turned northwards to Edinburgh. Braidwood was offered, and quickly accepted, a salary of £400 a year to become superintendent of the new London brigade. He took up his post in June 1832. Braidwood's new command was operational in

Fireman of Vision – I. James Braidwood who came from Edinburgh in 1832 to command the infant London Fire Engine Establishment until killed by a falling wall in the great Tooley Street fire of 1861 (London Fire Brigade)

January 1833 and by any terms it was a large one. He had at his initial disposal 80 full-time firemen, based at 19 fire stations. There were also to be two fireboats on the Thames to help protect the huge flammable riverside warehouse risks. Each insurance company was expected to pay a subscription of £8,000 per year towards the cost of the new brigade.

This progress, however welcome, only took direct account of property risk. Although firemen carried out rescues at fires as a matter of course, the whole structure of fire-fighting was still very much geared to the primary task of restricting the fire damage and loss to buildings. In the face of growing fatalities and injury in fires, it was rather surprising that the first moves to set up a separate Fire Escape Society took place in London in 1828, not as an adjunct to the need for better organised fire-fighting but as an entirely independent initiative.

As a result, the Royal Society for the Protection of Life from Fire was founded in 1836. It was funded by voluntary contributions and initially, on an income of £800 a year, the society provided six mobile wheeled 60ft (18m) escape ladders in central London. These were located at strategic street sites such as large squares, and were manned almost continuously by 'conductors'. When a fire alarm was raised, therefore, not only did the fire brigade need to be summoned but the wheeled escape ladder also. This would be hurriedly pushed to

A ROYAL SUMMONS

On the evening of 19 March 1853 Braidwood and the London Fire Engine Establishment received a telegraph from the Prince Consort at Windsor Castle, where a small fire in the servants' quarters in the Prince of Wales Tower had got out of hand, despite the frantic efforts of a battalion of Guards and nine fire engines from the Castle and Windsor beyond.

After an hour's struggle, their attempts at fire-fighting did not appear to have had any effect. The fire was still raging, and as it started to spread out into the East Terrace, Prince Albert sent for Braidwood. All had been evacuated but the Queen was in residence with the royal family. Albert, who had been closely involved in the initial fire-fighting, clearly feared for the Castle as he summoned Braidwood and his men.

Although the telegraphic request went via Paddington and the Great Western Railway, and by indirect route to Braidwood's City headquarters in Watling Street, no time was lost. He immediately mobilised and harnessed two of his most powerful pumps, crewed by ten experienced firemen, and galloped through the darkened London streets to the London and South Western's Waterloo railway station. From there he was directed to Nine Elms Depot at Battersea, where a special train including horse boxes was waiting.

It was not until 1.30am that the London crews finally arrived at Windsor Castle and by then the fire was under some control. However, there can be no doubt that when at dawn the fire was finally extinguished, Braidwood and his men had played their part in saving Windsor Castle from complete devastation.

the scene of the fire – no easy task, as the contraptions weighed 18cwt (914kg) and were unwieldy, especially on gradients and over cobblestones. However, public subscriptions were plentiful towards the Royal Society and its escape ladders, and as the London Fire Engine Establishment developed and expanded, so too did the escape stations with as many as 85 separate bases across London by 1850. In their first 20 years, no fewer than 972 lives were saved by these escapes.

Braidwood encouraged the society to retain the responsibility for rescue. He was ever-concerned with developing the equipment and expertise of his own command, which grew increasingly busy in dealing with outbreaks of fire right across the capital.

Braidwood also continued to strive to improve the working conditions of his men. In the early 1830s, the colourful yet highly impractical insurance-company uniform livery was replaced by a more functional black tunic, leather helmet and knee-boots. Braidwood even provided a silk neck-scarf to prevent sparks from getting down firemen's necks. His men, whilst having to suffer intense discipline, were well paid – 21s a week, with further payment for seniority. Promotion was through the ranks, and there was even then a pension scheme. Not surprisingly, there was a waiting list to join.

But over his two decades and more in command of the London Fire Engine Establishment, Braidwood continued to resist changes with which he had not been personally associated. Throughout his years in London he continually rejected steam power, which by 1860 was very well developed. Many notable varieties of reliable steam fire-pumps were now being built for use in many larger and well-populated urban areas of the United Kingdom, but Braidwood would not introduce them into his brigade, still preferring to rely on well-tried manual pumps.

Braidwood became an Associate of the Institution of Civil Engineers; he read technical papers on fire matters to the Royal Society of Arts, and was generally in demand as an acknowledged expert in his field.

Sadly, Braidwood's reign came to a tragic and sudden end. At about 5 o'clock in the afternoon of Saturday 22 June 1861, a small fire was discovered in Scovell's warehouse in Tooley Street, Southwark. This was close to London Bridge on the south bank of the Thames and, ironically, directly opposite to the very spot on the north bank where the terrible inferno of 1666 had started.

The first units of Braidwood's brigade quickly found that the fire was spreading rapidly into floors above and below the original outbreak, fuelled by the highly flammable contents of the huge dockside warehouse. These included 10,000 casks of tallow, hundreds of sacks of sugar, saltpetre, jute, tea and flour. The building itself was a veritable tinder-box. Early attempts were made to

FIRE DOGS

Many firemen on London's fire stations during the nineteenth century kept pets, and by far the most popular were dogs. Quite a few dogs would develop a liking for the excitement of fire-fighting and when a fire call came in would run alongside the horses as they strained to pull the fire engines and firemen towards the address of the fire.

One of the most famous dogs was Chance, which had been discovered by some watermen marooned by a rising tide at Blackfriars Pier. They cared for the dog and it remained with them as they plied their waterborne trade. However, before long they enrolled as firemen in James Braidwood's London Fire Engine Establishment and the dog went too. Chance became 'stationed' at the Watling Street Fire Station and over the next ten years became a much-loved character.

He would follow firemen into burning buildings and whenever there was a collapsed ruin to search, Chance would help pull burning timbers away in the search for casualties. It is reputed that he suffered no less than six broken legs, yet each time returned to active 'duty'. In the brigade there went a song:

> Stop me not but onward let me jog,
> For I am Chance, the London Fireman's
>   dog.

Chance's eyesight eventually began to fail, and legend has it that he died under the wheels of the horse-drawn fire pump that he had guided for almost a decade.

His body was stuffed and mounted, and for many years was used to raise funds for the widows and orphans of firemen killed in the course of duty.

section off the more fire-vulnerable stock by sliding iron doors although, neglectfully, some of these had been left ajar. In no time the fire had leapt across the narrow alleyways that abounded in this part of dockland and was igniting adjacent warehouses, each well stocked with oils and paints. By the time that the first fire-fighting jets were brought into play to protect the adjoining buildings from the already intense heat, it was obvious that Braidwood's men had a battle on their hands.

Within one hour of the outbreak, virtually all personnel of the London Fire Engine Establishment were at the scene: some 117 firemen, 27 horse-drawn manual pumps, 28 hand-propelled pumps, and 2 floating pumps on the Thames. Several pumps and firemen from private and volunteer brigades also arrived during the first two hours to join in the fray.

At about 5.30 pm Braidwood had arrived at the scene to take personal command, and was quickly directing his firemen and attempting to co-ordinate the collective efforts to quell the fearsome and destructive advance of the fire. As with all large fires, huge crowds flocked to the area, hampering fire-fighting efforts and adding to the general confusion and chaos. By 7 o'clock, the inferno had spread along 1,000yd (914m) of dockside

A contemporary print of the great Tooley Street riverside fire of 22 June 1861 in which Braidwood was killed. The fire caused £2 million damage in the huge warehouses, an enormous sum for those days (London Fire Brigade)

A RIVAL BRIGADE

During the period of the 1850s, when Braidwood's brigade was under great pressure to provide an efficient yet low-cost service for the expanding capital, several well-found 'private' brigades sprang up. One of the most effective of these was that of the Hodges Gin Distillery in Lambeth.

Led by 'Captain' Hodges, it was served by forty employees of the distillery who first manned two manual pumps when the brigade was inaugurated in 1851. It was primarily set up to provide fire cover for the distillery, itself a huge risk; but with the profits of his company to spend, Hodges found that fires and fire-fighting became his main purpose in life.

His activities attracted the Duke of Sutherland who, when in London, would spend some time at the fire station in the distillery, doubtless hoping to get a 'run out'. Hodges was not slow to look to the future either, and in 1862 replaced his two manual pumps with two of the very first steamer pumps to see service in London. They were named 'Deluge' and 'Torrent'.

Braidwood, who had died the previous year at the huge inferno at Tooley Street, had strongly resisted the onset of steam power, but Hodges's two pumps were admired both in London and on the frequent occasions in 1862 when one was taken further afield for demonstration purposes.

On one such visit, 'Deluge' was taken as far as Plymouth to display its impressive potential, where, with a full head of steam, it powered a vertical water jet some 130 feet high, whilst delivering 140 gallons per minute.

In the distillery, from the top of a 120 feet high observation tower from which much of London could be viewed, Hodges had a constant watch kept for fire outbreaks.

The Hodges brigade was so quick in turning out that it was not unknown for it to beat Braidwood's men to the scene. There were, of course, many incidents where the firemen of the London Fire Engine Establishment were glad to see the two powerful Hodges pumps. These played a significant part in many London fires of the period, being used on almost four hundred occasions between 1862 and 1865.

BRAIDWOOD'S BUTTONS

Braidwood was killed instantly and his body remained unrecovered for three days after the fatal building collapse during the Tooley Street conflagration of 22 June 1861. This was partly because many tons of compacted masonry and timber had fallen in the initial collapse, and because other subsequent falls had taken place, making the entire area unsafe for recovery and salvage work until the huge fire had been extinguished.

On 25 June, after hours of careful digging, clearing and shoring up, all having to be done by hand, Braidwood's body was at last located and slowly uncovered amid the still-warm stone and brickwork.

Once the body of London's Fire Chief was ready to be lifted out into a waiting coffin, the last act was the removal of his fire tunic buttons. These were cut off by the supervising officer and distributed to the final rescue party as a sombre keepsake of the tragedy.

Braidwood's silk neckerchief was also retained, and today is displayed in the London Fire Brigade museum, its bloodstains still a visible reminder of the day that disaster befell the London Fire Engine Establishment and its able and courageous leader.

warehouses, and even in the light of this summer evening the glow could be seen from Epsom, some twenty miles to the south.

At about 7.30, with the fire still burning out of control, Braidwood was leading a crew of firemen down a smoke-filled side street when a masonry gable-end wall weighing some fifty tons (tonnes) came crashing down, scattering all in its fateful path. Braidwood could not escape and was buried under the hot and smouldering debris, there to end his historic fire-fighting career. His body could not be recovered for three days, by which time the fire had been surrounded, controlled and finally extinguished. Eleven acres (4.4ha) of warehouses were entirely destroyed, and as big an area again was in part fire- or smoke-damaged. The cost of the insured fire loss was put at over £2 million – a huge sum in those days.

Braidwood's funeral was an even bigger event than the fire. Queen Victoria was represented by the Duke of Sutherland and the Earl of Caithness, and every church in the City tolled its largest bell in tribute. The funeral procession to Abney Park Cemetery was 1½ miles (2.4km) in length, and virtually halted the capital. There were almost all Braidwood's firemen, 1,000 policemen, 700 men of the London Rifle Brigade (including Braidwood's three sons), the band of the Society for the Protection of Life from Fire, and mourners from almost every social class and background. Tributes arrived from as far afield as Australia. London's first fire chief was thus buried with full honours and with considerable pomp not normally accorded outside the aristocracy.

Braidwood's successor was to enjoy an even greater reputation.

Captain Eyre Massey Shaw

Following the Tooley Street conflagration, the Home Secretary, Sir George Grey, set up a Select Committee to look into the need for a more widely funded fire brigade for London – not one just supported and maintained by the insurance companies. The Select Committee sat during April 1862 and duly submitted its findings one month later. Its primary recommendations were for a professional brigade to be formed under the control of the Commissioners of Police, and for there to be clear Parliamentary control over budgets and manpower. The area covered by the new brigade was proposed to be that of the Metropolitan Board of Works, the forerunner of the London County Council.

However, before these recommendations could gather dust there was a heated debate as to whether it was ethical for the police to be in charge also of London's fire brigade. Even by this time there were numerous such joint bodies in provincial cities and towns, protecting the public both from the criminal and from acts of fire. Why not also for the capital?

TOO LATE

The Bridgwater Fire Brigade received a call a short time since to a fire at Ashdown Farm. Attempts were made in vain for some time to procure horses to convey the engine. At length a firm was found willing to allow the use of their animals, but the result was far from encouraging, as the rapid pace at which they were driven caused the death of one of the horses. The Fire Brigade reached the scene two hours after the outbreak. – *Fire and Water*, October 1891

Fireman of Vision — II. Captain (later Sir) Eyre Massey Shaw, KCB, socialite and friend of the Prince of Wales, who led the firemen of the Metropolitan Fire Brigade for twenty-five years from 1866 until his resignation in 1891 (Fire Protection Association)

But Parliament dithered over progress of the Select Committee's findings, and meanwhile the insurance companies were anxious to appoint Braidwood's successor. After some consideration of likely candidates, the appointments board turned to Ireland and offered the post to Captain Eyre Massey Shaw, a 31-year-old who at that time was in command of Belfast's combined police and fire brigade. Shaw had an interesting background, having studied engineering and science at Trinity College, Dublin. After service in the North Cork Rifles, he had turned his attention to police and fire brigade matters. He was a natural leader of men, although rather gruff in manner, and with an obvious independence of spirit.

Captain Shaw took up his post as Chief Officer of the London Fire Engine Establishment in May 1862, and moved into a residence over the headquarters station in Watling Street in the City. He very quickly showed himself to be a charismatic personality, and soon became known as the 'Long 'Un' on account of his tall and slender frame. Shaw's silver-grey goatee beard and long moustache undoubtedly enhanced his impressive physical appearance. Somewhat more praiseworthily, Shaw also had bestowed upon him the title of 'Fire King', as his thinking and influence on fire-fighting and fire-safety matters made him the acknowledged expert in his field.

The Select Committee's Report to create a larger brigade for London still gave Shaw much difficulty. Despite the committee's view that such an enlarged force should be under police control, Shaw drew up an establishment scheme for the proposed new brigade's area of 117sq miles (303km^2). The existing London Fire Engine Establishment covered only 10sq miles (26km^2) of Central London, including the City. Shaw's plan was for forty-three fire stations to provide cover for the larger area of the metropolis and this total was to incorporate the existing seventeen stations of the LFEE. The present 129 firemen would be increased to 232, and Shaw's scheme was originally costed at £70,000 a year.

Sir George Grey, the Home Secretary, would have none of such a big sum and sent Shaw away to rethink his proposals. Eventually, Grey agreed to go ahead and promote a bill to create the new brigade on the basis of an annual cost of £50,000, of which the government was to contribute £10,000. The insurance companies were also each expected to pay an annual sum of £10,000.

Despite Shaw's reluctance to accept the task of setting up the bigger brigade under such parsimonious conditions, he eventually agreed after it became clear that there would not be any police involvement. 'The Act for the Establishment of a fire brigade in the Metropolis' became law during July 1865. Thus was born not only the modern forerunner of today's London Fire Brigade, but also the first basic legal responsibility on the part of a local authority – the Metropolitan Board of Works – to provide and maintain an efficient force of firemen. For the first time, too, a fireman's duty was to save life as well as property.

Shaw was the natural and unsurprising choice to take command of the new Metropolitan Fire Brigade, now easily the largest professional fire-fighting force in the United Kingdom. It formally came into being on 1 January 1866 and Shaw lost no time in setting an amazing pace of life as its leader. He devoted much of his day to the problems of recruiting and setting up the new brigade, and would personally take command at every large fire in the capital. Slowly, the new force came together and Shaw introduced many new features. Horsedrawn steam pumps replaced the manual pumps so beloved of Braidwood, although a number of manuals were retained as back-up appliances.

Shaw rationalised the fire-fighting uniform of the brigade. Gone was the rather plain black uniform tunic of Braidwood's days, replaced by a brass-buttoned navy-blue tunic and trousers, leather boots, black belt, and axe in pouch. A standard working rig was also introduced for wear during training and station duties. The firemen's fire kit was topped by Shaw's first uniform love – brass helmets – although he and his four superintendents all wore silver versions.

THE TURNOUT TO A FIRE – 1870 STYLE

Had the fire been distant, they would have had to commence their gallop somewhat leisurely, for fear of breaking down the horses; but it was not far off – not much more than a couple of miles – so they dashed round the corner of their own street at a brisk trot, and swept into Oxford Street. Here they broke into a gallop, and here the noise of their progress began, for the great thoroughfare was crowded with vehicles and pedestrians, many of whom were retiring from the theatres and music-halls, and other places of entertainment.

To pass through such a crowd without coming into collision with anything required not only the most dexterous driving, but rendered it necessary that some of the men on the engine should stand up and shout, or rather roar, incessantly, as they whirled along, clearing everything out of their way, and narrowly escaping innumerable crashes by a mere hairbreadth.

The men, as we said before, having been sailors, seemed to shout with the memory of the boatswain strong upon them, for their tones were pitched in the deepest and gruffest bass key. Sometimes there was a lull for a moment, as a comparatively clear space of a hundred yards or so lay before them; then their voices rose like the roaring of the gale as a stupid or deaf cabman got in their way, or a plethoric 'bus threatened to interrupt their furious passage.

The cross streets were the points where the chief difficulties met them. There the cab and van drivers turned into or crossed the great thoroughfare, all ignorant of the thunderbolt that was rushing on like a fiery meteor, with its lamps casting a glare of light before, and the helmets of its stern charioteers flashing back the rays of street lamps and windows; for, late though the hour was, all the gin palaces and tobacconist's shops, and many of the restaurants, were still open and brightly illuminated.

At the corner of Wells Street, the crowd of cabs and other vehicles was so great that the driver of the engine began to tighten his reins, and Jim Baxmore and Joe Corney raised their voice to a fierce shout. Cabs, 'busses, and pedestrians scattered right and left in a marvellous manner; the driver slackened his reins, cracked his whip, and the horses stretched out again.

In passing Berners Street, a hansom cab swept round the corner, its dashing driver smoking a cigar in sublime self-satisfaction, and looking carelessly right and left for a 'fare'. This exquisite almost ran into the engine! There was a terrific howl from all the firemen; the cabby turned his smart horse with a bound to one side, and lost his cigar in the act – in reference to which misfortune he was heartily congratulated by a small member of the Shoeblack Brigade – while the engine went steadily and sternly on its way.

'There, it shows a light,' observed one of the firemen to Dale, as he pointed to a luminous appearance in the sky away to the north-east.

Dale was already looking in that direction, and made no reply.

As they approached Tottenham Court Road, the driver again checked the pace a little, yet even at the reduced speed they passed everything like a whirlwind. The traffic here was so great that it behoved them to be more cautious. Of course, the more need that there was for caution, the more necessity was there for shouting; and the duty of Baxmore and Corney – standing as they did in front of their comrades beside the driver– became severe, but they had good lungs both of them!

At the point where Tottenham Court Road cuts Oxford Street the accumulation of vehicles of all sorts, from a hand-barrow to a furniture van, is usually very great. To one unaccustomed to the powers of London drivers, it would have seemed nothing short of madness to drive full tilt into the mass that blocked the streets at this point. But the firemen did it. They reined up a little, it is true, just as a hunter does in gathering his horse together for a rush at a stone wall, but there was nothing like an approach to stopping.

'Hi! Hi!! HI!!!' roared the firemen, Baxmore and Corney high above the rest. A 'bus lumbered to the left just in time; a hansom sprang to the right, not a moment too soon; a luggage van bolted into Crown Street; the pedestrians scattered right and left, and the way was clear – no, not quite clear! The engine had to turn at a right angle here into Tottenham Court Road. Round it went on the two off-wheels, and came full swing on a market-gardener and a hot-coffee woman, who were wheeling their respective barrows leisurely side by side, and chatting as they went.

The roar that burst from the firemen was terrific. The driver attempted both to pull up and to turn aside. The market-gardener dropt his barrow and fled. The hot-coffee woman, being of a resolute nature, thrust her barrow by main force on the footpath, and so saved her goods and herself by a hair-breadth, while the barrow of her friend was knocked in pieces. But the effort of the engine-driver to avoid this had well-nigh resulted in serious consequences. In endeavouring to clear the market-gardener he drew so near to the footpath that in another moment a lamp-post would have been carried away and the wheels of the engine, in all probability, knocked off, had not Joe Corney observed the danger.

With a truly Irish yell Joe seized the rein next him, and pulled the horses round almost at a right angle. The nave of the hind-wheel just shaved the post as it flew by. The whole thing passed so swiftly that before the market-gardener recovered from his consternation the engine was only discernible in the distance by the sparks that flew from its wheels as it held on in its furious way.

All long its course a momentary disturbance of London equanimity was created. Families not yet abed rushed to their front window and, looking out, exclaimed, 'Ha! the firemen.' Tipplers in gin palaces ran to the doors and said 'There they go!' 'That's your sort!' 'Hurrah, my hearties!' or 'Go it, ye cripples!' according to the different stages of inebriation at which they had arrived; and belated men of business stopped to gaze, and then resumed their way with thoughts and speculations on fire and fire insurance, more or less deep and serious according to temperament. But the disturbance was only temporary. The families retired to their suppers or beds, the tipplers returned to their tipple, the belated speculators to their dreams, and in a few minutes, no doubt, forgot what they had seen, and forgot, perchance, that they had any personal interest in fire-raising, or fire extinction, or fire prevention, or fire in any dangerous shape or form whatever; or indulged in the comforting belief, mayhap, that whatever disasters might attend the rest of the London community, they and their houses being endued with the properties of the salamander, nothing in the shape of fire might, could, would or should kindle upon them. So true is it that 'all men think all men mortal but themselves'.

From *Fighting the Flames*
R. M. Ballantyne (1870)

FAREWELL FROM THE FIRE KING

On 30 October 1891, Eyre Massey Shaw was knighted. He arrived in the recreation room at Southwark that evening to find as many men as could be spared – three hundred of them – gathered to wish him well.

Shaw read his speech in a voice which was surprisingly faltering for a man who had commanded at so many great fires:

Shadows may come across your route, mists and fogs may obscure the vision of those in charge, the darkness of night may come down and obscure her on every side, yet there is a compass on board, and those in charge can continue their course onward, confidently and patiently, until the mists disperse and the day dawns . . .

You know your duty. Your position here is this. The inhabitants of this vast metropolis numbering some five million persons, desire to be protected from the ravages of fire and have employed you for the purpose . . . It is your duty always to be loyal . . .

An excerpt from
London's Noble Fire Brigades 1833–1904
by Sally Holloway

The disciplinary régime of the new brigade was extremely harsh and arduous. Men worked a continuous duty system and were often not out of uniform for days on end. Leave of a few hours was granted from time to time, although married men were able to live on the fire stations in very basic married quarters. New recruits were now being drawn only from the ranks of ex-sailors, whose previous hardy existence prepared them well for life in the London brigade where long duty periods, teamwork, physical strength and the ability to work at heights and under dangerous conditions were mandatory.

Significant progress and improvements made by Shaw in 1867 included the acquisition of the street escape-ladders of the Society for the Protection of Life. The existing conductors who manned the escape posts were replaced by Shaw's uniformed firemen. Another major advance was the introduction of telegraphic links between all Shaw's fire stations, and although at first this was a rather ponderous device, it was more positive and accurate than sending boy-runners with messages. The system was to remain in use for over forty years until replaced by the telephone.

By the end of 1869, Shaw had established 54 fire stations, together with the escape-ladder posts, across the 117sq miles (303km^2) of London, and his brigade was effective and well trained. Before long, he, his brigade and the science of fire-fighting, found themselves the focus of attention of society gentlemen and, in particular, two enthusiastic and addicted fire 'buffs', the Duke of Sutherland and the Earl of Caithness. During the 1870s, mechanisation and steam power were being impressively developed by Shaw and his officers, and London's gentlemen viewed the whole fire scene as something akin to a sport.

To have on one's country estate a fire brigade equipped with the latest steam fire-pump was all the rage at this time, and in 1875 there was even formed a London Auxiliary Fire Brigade. Shaw viewed with some disdain the various volunteer town and parish brigades on the outer fringes of his command for, although he had the legal power to take command of their numbers at any incident inside the London area, they were generally not equipped or trained up to the very high level of London's professional brigade. However, the London Auxiliary Fire Brigade was different. Right from its inception, its well-to-do members asked Shaw to guide their formation and the 'Fire King' not unnaturally insisted that the auxiliaries should attend regular Metropolitan Fire Brigade drill and training sessions, alongside regular fire-fighters. Shaw allowed the auxiliaries to attend fires but they had to take their instructions from Shaw's officers. The auxiliaries became an upper-class set of firemen, providing their own pumps, hose and uniforms.

The annual subscription to the élite crews was one guinea.

It is very probable that through the activity of the Duke of Sutherland and the Earl of Caithness in the London Auxiliaries, Shaw first met the Prince of Wales. The prince's set took enthusiastically to the physical rough and tumble of fire-fighting, and Shaw himself came from a very privileged and upper-class background. The prince quickly befriended London's fire chief, and by 1876 Shaw had a personal fire uniform with silver helmet placed ready for the Prince of Wales at Chandos Street fire station, Charing Cross, one of the busiest of all the Metropolitan regular stations.

There also seems little doubt that the Prince of Wales, along with the duke and the earl, would occasionally spend several hours during an evening with the firemen of Chandos Street, enjoying a game of billiards and waiting for that nerve-tingling moment when a fire call would come in. On those occasions when there was a serious outbreak of fire in the capital and the prince was in residence at Marlborough House, Shaw would have the prince's fire uniform collected from Chandos Street by a carriage that then went on to collect the royal fire-fighter and proceed in haste to the scene of the conflagration. The Prince of Wales's fire-fighting activities were probably unknown to the public at large, apart that is from the firemen of the brigade who, no doubt, enjoyed the fine cigars that the prince passed round after a successful battle against the flames.

1876 was a significant year for London's brigade as it saw the go-ahead for a new headquarters for Shaw in Southwark. In the same year, Shaw published one of his most important works, a massive treatise called *Fire Protection – A Complete Manual of the Organisation, Machinery, Discipline and General Working of the Fire Brigade of London*. The book was the first authentic collation of training and fire-fighting techniques and was to bring many requests for Shaw to visit lesser brigades up and down the land, not least the many country-house fire brigades of the aristocracy, many of whom knew Shaw personally.

As Shaw constantly strove for better equipment and more firemen to combat the growing number of fires with their subsequent deaths and injuries, he found his path constantly impeded and obstructed by the politicians of the Metropolitan Board of Works. Time and again they refused the funds to expand the force as Shaw desired and in 1876, the home secretary, fearful of a major London fire disaster, placed the matter before yet another Select Committee. Its 1,000-page report and recommendations again caused a great stir. One of its main suggestions was to increase the rate for the upkeep of the brigade, as well as recommending that it should have responsibility for water supplies, including the

THE FIREMEN'S ADAGE

'A fireman, to be successful, must enter buildings. He must get in below, above, on every side; from opposite houses, over back walls, over side walls, through panels of doors, through windows, through skylights, through holes cut by himself in gates, walls and the roof. He must know how to reach the attic from the basement by ladders placed on half-burned stairs, and the basement from the attic by a rope made fast on a chimney. His whole success depends on his getting in and remaining there, and he must always carry his appliances with him, as without them he is of no use.' – *Sir Eyre Massey Shaw, KCB, Chief Officer, 1861–1891 Metropolitan Fire Brigade (forerunner of the London Fire Brigade)*

installation of street fire hydrants. Like the 1862 inquiry, it also raised the question of a joint police and fire authority. The Report was much argued over but never implemented in totality, and Shaw continued to struggle to provide the service to which he felt Londoners were due. It was some consolation that he was made a Companion of the Order of the Bath in 1879.

It was also during this period that Shaw's preachings regarding undue fire risks and the need for greater fire-safety measures in theatres and other public places started to have effect. Over a number of years there had been several major London theatre fires, notably the Alhambra in Leicester Square on the night of 7 December 1882. Although the building took fire whilst empty of the public, two firemen were killed during operations. But in 1887 came a horrific fire tragedy that led directly to better theatre fire-safety provisions.

On the evening of 5 September 1887, a fire broke out backstage at the Theatre Royal, Exeter, during a packed house. The ensuing chaos both from the spreading smoke and fire, together with the stampede for the few exits, caused 188 deaths – still the worst theatre fire tragedy in the world. Shaw was immediately asked to attend the following morning and, after a detailed investigation at Exeter, he went on to produce for the home secretary a damning and far-reaching report that led to a new statute coming into effect. This required properly marked theatre exits and regular inspections of such and, later on, a descending safety curtain.

Once the new Southwark headquarters of the brigade was commissioned in 1877, Shaw was able to entertain his gentry friends in a fitting style. Once a week, Shaw would lay on a spectacular drill display, and lords and ladies would flock to see the brigade exercising its skills. The Prince of Wales was a frequent visitor at these weekly events, which were very much part of the London social scene of that time.

Some idea of how busy the brigade was can be gauged by the total number of fires dealt with during 1878 – some 4,199. It is also interesting that some 2,500 of these were 'small' outbreaks which were quickly dealt with by horse-drawn manual hand pumps, which were still in use in some number. By this year, Shaw's force totalled 48 fire stations and 107 fire-escape ladder stations. There were by now also 4 fire tugs on the Thames, in readiness for the ever-present risk of fire in the tinder-dry and dense riverside warehouse area that had claimed Shaw's predecessor.

London's fire chief travelled to New York and the east coast of the United States in 1882, to view American fire-fighting methods and fire-safety awareness. On his return he was critical of the height of the early tower-blocks of several US cities. By this stage Shaw had already visited a number of European countries, but he

THE FIREMAN PRINCE AND A NEAR MISS

One of the largest London blazes of the 1880s engulfed the Alhambra Theatre in Leicester Square right in the heart of London's theatreland on the cold and icy night of 7 December 1882.

The fire had been discovered by a night-watchman about an hour after the last of the audience had left. Fortunately, no-one was trapped by the spreading smoke and flames.

Very soon, the first steam pumps of Massey Shaw's Metropolitan Fire Brigade were at work but the fire rapidly took hold and soon threatened many surrounding buildings. Within forty minutes of the first alarm, twenty-five pumps and one hundred and fifty firemen were at the scene.

Around midnight Shaw, on learning of the escalating nature of the incident, summoned his carriage and drove quickly from his Southwark headquarters to Leicester Square, to take command personally. But before leaving Southwark, he sent an urgent message to Marlborough House for the Prince of Wales to be informed. Shaw knew that Prince Edward was 'in town'. Once at the fire, Shaw sent his driver first to Chandos Street fire station nearby to collect the royal fire uniform and pick up the Prince. Shaw was certain that the royal fireman would not want to miss this one.

Sure enough, about thirty minutes later, the Prince of Wales – resplendent in his silver helmet and brass-buttoned fire tunic and leather boots – was escorted to where London's fire chief was co-ordinating the battle against the flames. These now engulfed not only the Alhambra but also premises in several side streets off Leicester Square. Apart from wearing his identifying silver helmet, the Prince took on an anonymous presence amid the swirling smoke and sparks, and among the brass-helmeted throng of fire-fighters manning water jets, tending steam pumps or getting even more street hydrants coupled up.

About thirty minutes after his arrival, the Prince of Wales, accompanied by Assistant Superintendent Ashford, was moving warily down a smoky courtyard towards the rear of the doomed theatre. A damp mist from the massed water jets rained down as they stepped carefully over hoses that threaded the pavements in all directions. As the Prince stopped to speak to a group of firemen struggling to work two jets into the upper windows at the rear of the Alhambra at third floor level, from which orange flames licked forth, the first warning of disaster came.

Crumbling fragments of stone and several slates and tiles came crashing down all around the fire-fighters. As one they tucked their chins into their chests and braced themselves for a further fall of debris from above. But this time it was no few slates and tiles but the entire fire-blackened gable-end wall of the Alhambra that was poised to break away and thunder downwards into the narrow courtyard below.

The partial collapse of the end wall struck eight of the firemen, burying three under the hot lumps of stone and timber. Mercifully, Assistant Superintendent Ashford managed to push the Prince of Wales into the relative shelter of the face of the opposite building in the courtyard when the first fragments fell, and he was unhurt though badly shaken.

The firemen manning the powerful and reactive water jets could not leave their posts to succour the group struck and buried by the fall. It took about half-an-hour to extricate the badly injured firemen, whose rescue was led by Shaw, with the Prince one of those lending a hand, heaving stonework and timber off the trapped men. While this work was in progress, the fire burgeoned out and up into the night sky above the rescue operation, a pyrotechnic display unseen in London since the Tooley Street fire of 1861. Another ten steam pumps and fifty firemen were called in as precautionary reinforcements, although by 2.30 am the fire had been surrounded.

Much later on that morning, and accompanied by Shaw, the Prince of Wales visited the seven injured firemen in Charing Cross Hospital. Both the heir to the throne and Shaw wore sombre dark suits and top hats as they briefly spoke to five of the injured men. The other two were still unconscious and gravely ill. Prince Edward left seven large boxes of cigars for them, and then went on with Shaw to view the smouldering remains of the Alhambra Theatre nearby.

Sadly, the two badly injured firemen, one of whom was the Prince's guide Ashford, died from their injuries soon after, but all the others recovered, and eventually returned to operational fire-fighting.

The famous oil painting 'Saved' painted by Charles Vigor in 1890 and exhibited at the Royal Academy in 1892. It depicts a fireman of the Metropolitan Fire Brigade carrying out a posed rescue on what is generally accepted as the steps of Massey Shaw's Winchester House headquarters in Southwark. Eventually, it was acquired by the Borough of Southport who donated the painting in 1972 to the Fire Service College where it now hangs in the dining hall (Fire Service College, Moreton-in-Marsh)

found the American experience not at all to his liking.

Ever the innovator, Shaw introduced a new round-thread coupling for fire hoses which speeded up this essential task. He also pioneered the use of chemical fire extinguishers. From his desk at Southwark, he set himself a punishing schedule of visits, meetings and demonstrations, and quite frequently worked very late into the night, only to be disturbed by a summons to a large fire.

In the spring of 1882, Queen Victoria invited Shaw to Osborne House on the Isle of Wight to inspect the fire-protection arrangements. On the conclusion of his visit, he was received in audience by Her Majesty, and on Shaw's return to his London duties soon after, he received from the queen a personal gift of an inscribed clock. Today this timepiece still has pride of place in Shaw's London home, Winchester House, now the London Fire Brigade's permanent museum.

In November 1882, Shaw was also immortalised in Gilbert's words in *Iolanthe*. A section of verse sung by the Fairy Queen goes:

> Oh, Captain Shaw!
> Type of true love kept under!
>   Could thy Brigade
>   With cold cascade
> Quench my great love, I wonder!

SHAW AT LARGE

Shaw insisted that every fire station and street escape ladder should report its availability twice a day so that he could be absolutely certain that fire cover was properly spread and, of course, be aware of any defective equipment.

On one occasion, he noticed that an escape ladder at Whitechapel Church had not been 'booked available'. Shaw telegraphed to the Superintendent of the district, who confirmed at once that the escape was ready and manned. But Shaw was not satisfied and, no doubt mindful of setting an example, he ordered the escape ladder concerned to be wheeled to his Southwark headquarters some two miles away so that he could physically see it.

Two miles may not sound very far, but the escape weighed some eighteen hundredweights (900kg) and many streets had cobbled surfaces. Furthermore the ladders were fairly unstable and had no brakes.

When the two firemen arrived in full uniform in a sweaty and weary state at Southwark, Shaw sent them straight back with the escape to Whitechapel. Needless to say, word very quickly got around that the twice-daily return carried its penalty for any irregularity.

Shaw also spent a considerable amount of time visiting stations and personally conducting drill sessions. One evening when moving between fire stations, he arrived at his next destination whilst a telegraph was punching out the message: 'Watch out – the Long 'Un is out visiting. He may look you up'. Shaw stood impassively in the station watchroom and telegraphed back: 'With thanks. I have received your message. The Chief Officer'.

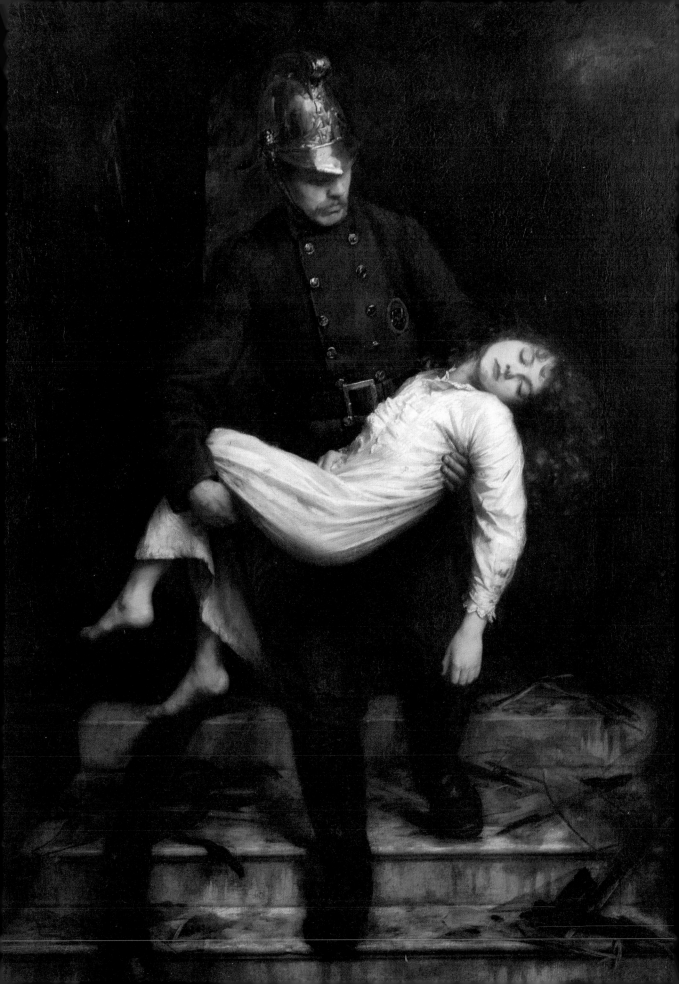

TWO FIREMEN OF VISION

A horse-drawn steam pump of the Metropolitan Fire Brigade and its crew get to work to provide water at a fire, circa 1890. Note the hose connection (left) from the water main and fire hoses feeding from the pump supply (right), together with the enthusiastic crowd and restraining 'bobby' (far left) (Fire Protection Association)

Life-saving progress. The original 50ft street based fire escapes were first placed on horse drawn chassis around 1895 and based at fire stations, making many street escapes redundant. Note the paired horses and small bells on the harness. Southwark Headquarters, Metropolitan Fire Brigade circa 1900 (London Fire Brigade)

Shaw, needless to say, was present at the first night, and for once appeared quite unnerved by all this operatic attention.

Not so welcome, some four years later, was the news that Shaw had been cited as co-respondent in a divorce case involving Lady Campbell. Also cited were the Marquis of Blandford and a General Butler. Shaw found himself in the headlines for other than fire reasons, although after a very protracted case neither party was granted a decree. Shaw, in fact, was married with four sons and two daughters.

Happily, the royal approbation of Shaw and the brigade held good, for on 25 May 1889 there took place a royal review by the Prince and Princess of Wales on Horse Guards Parade. Shaw himself led 100 picked firemen manning 22 horse-drawn steamers, 5 manual pumps and 5 hose vans, all immaculately turned out. The ceremony was to have included a gallop-past, and to have concluded with the presentation of gallantry and long-service medals. However, the crowds were so great that the jostling throng turned the event into a fiasco. The royal party, which also included the Princes Albert, Victor and George, and the Princesses Louise, Victoria and Maud, had great difficulty in reaching the dais. The event had to be curtailed in order to preserve some dignity, and afterwards Shaw was absolutely furious that this great 'first' had become so disorganised through the lack of sufficient police and military escorts. Questions were even asked in the House of Commons and, in a sense, this heralded the end of an era.

Earlier in 1889, the newly formed London County Council had replaced the Metropolitan Board of Works, which for twenty-two years Shaw had engaged in constant warfare for more funds and positive political support. For a while Shaw found the new London controlling body to be reasonable to his demands. Indeed, in 1890, the new council agreed to provide a number of new fire stations, 113 more firemen and to increase the number of street fire hydrants. But Shaw wanted more men to increase the usefulness of the escape-ladder stations, and he was also keen to replace the entire fire-engine fleet with steam pumps. Shaw soon found that apart from the early gesture, fresh finance was still going to be as scarce as under the old board.

Unfortunately relationships steadily worsened, and there was disquiet in both the ranks and amid Shaw's officers over the effects of the harsh financial régime.

Events came to a head in early 1891, when Shaw returned from another month-long overseas trip where he had been genuinely engaged in surveying various fire brigades' approaches to urban fire-fighting. The London County Council was clearly suspicious that Shaw had been holidaying abroad, which was one further straw in the wind. On 26 June 1891, Shaw wrote a short letter to

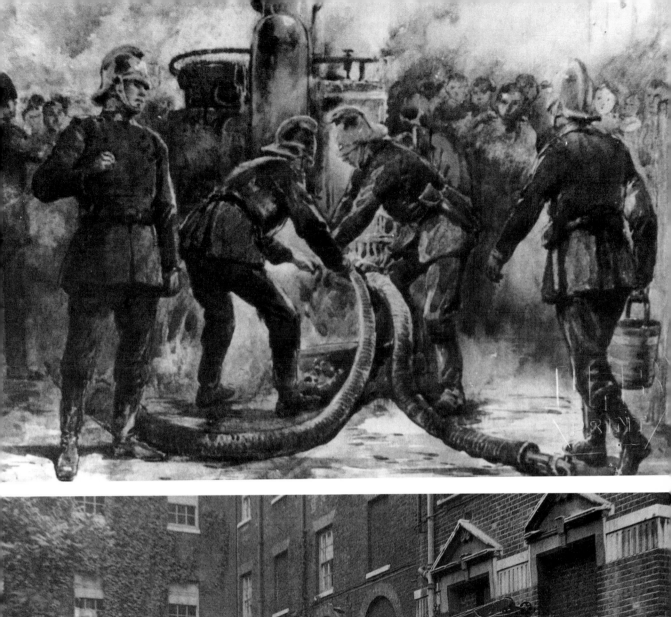

the London County Council, giving notice of his retirement. He was, after all, sixty years of age and he had led the capital's fire brigade for thirty years. In addition, an old fire-fighting leg injury was becoming troublesome. *Punch* paid Shaw a lengthy tribute in prose entitled 'The Fire King's Abdication', and commented that it would be appropriate to crown his career with a knighthood.

Shaw's last few weeks were eventful as he personally bade farewell to his officers and men, and to the many aristocrats whom he counted as his friends. There was even a chance to erase the memory of the awful Horse Guards Parade. At this time Shaw was the President of the National Fire Brigades Union and had been organising a review of firemen from all over the country, to be held at the Crystal Palace in July 1891. It was a glittering occasion, this time with the public properly marshalled and controlled and, to mark Shaw's last public event, the Prince of Wales graced the occasion accompanied by his cousin Kaiser Wilhelm II who, by all accounts, was also something of a fire enthusiast. The empress was also present on the saluting base, along with a number of dukes. Thus, as Shaw led the gallop-past of some of the most modern fire-engines of the time, he must have been an extremely proud and satisfied man. *Punch's* prediction was right, for Shaw's knighthood was conferred on the very day he retired from the brigade – 30 October 1891.

During his thirty eventful years in command of London's brigade, Shaw had laid the foundations of modern fire-fighting. Moreover, he handed on to the new generation of firemen a strong technological impetus as well as a proud heritage and noble tradition which was to stand firemen in good stead as they faced the challenges of the new century.

In 1904, the Metropolitan Fire Brigade changed its name to the London Fire Brigade and some five years later, King Edward VII and Queen Alexandra graced a Royal Review of the Brigade held in Hyde Park. Here the royal party arrive at the dais to present gallantry and long-service medals before watching a comprehensive drill display. Note the brass-helmeted younger member of the royal party. As the Prince of Wales, Edward had been to a number of large London fires with Massey Shaw. 10 July 1909 (London Fire Brigade)

3 FIREMEN AT WAR

Until the outbreak of World War I in 1914, firemen merely had a domestic role to play in rescues and fire-fighting at fires caused by human carelessness or disaster. But very early in the 1914–18 conflict the effects of modern warfare came for the first time to impinge on the lives of thousands far removed from the battlefront. The airship and then the aeroplane brought death and destruction to the home front, and the 1914–18 raids were serious although they were but a foretaste of what was to follow during the Blitzkrieg of 1940–5. In all this action, firemen found themselves thrust into the front line as they battled with the effects of aerial bombardment.

Such history was made in April 1915 when several zeppelin airships ventured over Dover, thus making the first air-raid ever on the United Kingdom. The few bombs that fell were dropped by hand from a fairly high altitude and, despite causing some widespread blast and fire damage, did not in any sense cause the local brigade much difficulty. However, on 31 May 1915 came a serious development when the first co-ordinated multiple zeppelin air-raid on London took place. One hundred and five separate premises in the Stoke Newington, Hoxton, Whitechapel and Shoreditch areas of the capital were hit by high explosive bombs. In a raid that lasted little more than an hour, four Londoners were killed and thirteen were seriously hurt. Hundreds of others were slightly injured.

EXHAUSTION

'It is strange when you are as exhausted as I am these days how little the opposite sex can mean to you. When I got back to London there was another heavy raid on. So I reported at Station 19 and they gave me a blanket on the floor of their control room.

I went to sleep and when I woke up I found myself next to a very lovely blonde. She was one of the control room girls, and in our sleep we had moved into each other's arms for warmth. So we stayed like that for the rest of the night, but as far as I was concerned it didn't mean a thing.

I must be getting old, or something.' – *Auxiliary Fireman Vic Flint, December 1940*

RECALL FROM THE COLOURS

During the early years of World War I, professional firemen who were Army or Navy Reservists were liable to be called to the colours, while a number of regular firemen volunteered for the armed services. Such departures were a serious drain on the trained manpower of brigades and it was not until the start of the regular zeppelin airship raids of 1915 that pressure was put on the government and the War Office to release these firemen so that they could bolster their brigade numbers back at home.

For a while the government resisted, preferring to increase those brigades so affected by locally-recruited volunteers, but when conscription was introduced in 1916 professional firemen were exempted.

However, following three serious London daylight raids in the summer of 1917, when the capital suffered a considerable loss of life as well as a large number of serious fires, the War Cabinet relented. An immediate recall was pronounced for all members of the London Fire Brigade who were serving in the armed forces. This welcome news soon saw three hundred men exchanging their army and navy uniforms for their more familiar brass helmets and navy brass-buttoned fire tunics. But by the time that most of these firemen were back crewing fire engines, the worst of the zeppelin and aircraft raids on the capital were over.

ROYAL PRAISE

The Duke of Kent opened the new Headquarters of Birmingham Fire Brigade on 2 December 1936, and took the opportunity publicly to praise the work of firemen. He stated that:

'. . . a fireman can no longer be classified purely as a manual labourer. The introduction of chemicals into the manufacture of so many goods, and the almost universal introduction of electricity demand a great deal of technical knowledge and high qualifications.

'Nowadays, it is not a case of waiting for a building to catch fire and then putting it out, but of methodically preparing through training for any possible outbreak. These careful preparations have replaced the *ad hoc* methods of fifty years ago.'

For the London Fire Brigade, this created a whole new arena in both rescue and fire-fighting. Twenty-five motor pumps and one hundred firemen were mobilised to the affected district, these crews facing problems not encountered before in a densely populated area. Apart from the blast-shattered factories, shops and terraced dwellings, there were fires burning fiercely all around, aided by escaping gas from damaged service mains. In addition, all surrounding premises were structurally unsafe and crumbling, due to the blast effect of the bombing. Many casualties were buried under the compacted debris of collapsed buildings underneath which fire was still burning. It was a horrendous situation for firemen to face.

Fortunately at this time the London Fire Brigade was probably the best trained and equipped in the world, manned entirely by professional fire-fighters, each in the mould of Massey Shaw. Although the fire situations were fairly straightforward to deal with, it was the rescue of buried or partially buried casualties that taxed firemen's skills. These were almost new rescue scenarios, where successful techniques of digging into rubble to locate live casualties and then to work towards their speedy release could only be developed with experience.

This was not long in being developed, as unhappily the zeppelins continued to raid London, the South East and the east coast regularly during the first two years of war. But worse was to come. In 1916, the first air-raid using aircraft took place over London, and although the bomb totals were not those of the zeppelin raids, for the first time aircraft began to drop incendiary devices mixed with high-explosive weapons. On 6 December 1917 alone, 270 small incendiary bombs dropped by 6 German aircraft caused a number of large fires in 30 different London boroughs, despite the relative inefficiency of the incendiaries. Most of these areas of the capital were protected by the London Fire Brigade, although localised town and borough brigades were also very active on this occasion. But probably the worst of the twenty-eight major air-raids of World War I hit central London on 4 January 1918. Odham's Press in Long Acre was one of many buildings that received a direct high-explosive hit, and several hundred incendiaries fell into gutters and onto roofs, each resulting in a separate outbreak of fire. Forty-one persons were killed outright and thirty-one bodies were subsequently recovered from damaged premises by firemen. There were over a hundred serious injuries, including several to firemen who had arrived soon after the fire bombs had fallen. The firemen had continued to work, comforting casualties, getting water jets to function and pitching ladders to upper floors to rescue people cut off by fire and the effects of explosion, even as the next wave of bombs fell out of the sky.

There were difficulties with providing a good, reliable supply of water to the motor pumps, as concussion damage caused local water mains to shatter. However, the London Fire Brigade called upon its large manpower resources to organise water relays from the nearest unaffected water supply and to provide the support teams of firemen needed to supplement the first rescue crews arriving at the scene of the bombing. Unfortunately, the borough brigades did not have the numbers of personnel that the London Fire Brigade enjoyed, and the bomb raids on their areas often saw the handful of firemen available soon overwhelmed by the enormity of the fire and rescue situation. In such cases, it was necessary for the public to pitch in to help, with some military assistance at the larger raids. Mutual reinforcement between fire brigades was yet to be an accepted part of the service scene.

All this new type of operational action for firemen between 1914 and 1918 was, however, absolutely nothing compared to what was to come to the home front and the civilian population during World War II. As the storm clouds gathered once again over Europe, the air-raids of the Spanish Civil War showed just how far advanced and deadly was the new aerial weaponry of war and its effect on the civilian population. Fire service conferences had been held as far back as 1933 to discuss and develop plans for combating future aerial bombing, but little had come of this initiative by the outbreak of World War II.

Fortunately, several eminent personalities added their own view of the need to prepare for air-raids on a scale as yet unforeseen. Amongst these was Professor J.B.S. Haldane, FRS, who made it quite clear in his book *Air Raid Precautions* of 1938 that the expansion of fire brigades was necessary. Somewhat comfortingly for firemen, Haldane stated that brigade personnel should not be expected to patrol the streets during actual air-raids!

In fact, the first positive pre-war governmental move to co-ordinate fire service readiness for war and the likely conflagrations that would ensue was in February 1937, when the Home Office required local authorities to submit Air Raid Precautions fire-protection schemes for their respective areas. There existed at this time 1,600 independent fire brigades in the United Kingdom under county council, district or parish control. These brigades ranged from such organisations as the London Fire Brigade with its full-time crews manning 106 pumping appliances, down to the solid-tyred ancient motor pump and handful of part-timers that typified many a rural brigade.

Two separate Acts of Parliament reinforced the urgency to prepare the fire service to meet the threat of war on the home front. The Air Raid Precautions Act of 1937 took effect on 1 January 1938 and made provision

HELMETS

By the end of the nineteenth century, virtually all fire brigades in the United Kingdom had adopted the 2½lb brass helmet as its standard fire fighting head protection.

However, with the coming of electricity and the growing danger of electrocution, it was surprising that it was not until June 1937 that the withdrawal of the ubiquitous brass helmet was started. It was replaced by a compressed cork pattern helmet safe to 15,000 volts and finished in black. These first appeared in the London Fire Brigade, where several firemen had been killed through electric shock received via their brass helmets.

The new helmets were gradually adopted throughout the bigger brigades, although firemen of a number of the small pre-war and volunteer brigades 'went to war' in 1939 still sporting brass helmets, but these were soon replaced by military steel helmets.

Today firemen wear tough yellow plastic helmets, and officers have white versions. Apart from being seen in museums, brass helmets are nowadays only rarely found in antique shops or at auctions, when they command considerable sums as collectors' items.

Fortuitously, a number of fire brigades retained a few brass helmets for ceremonial occasions.

LADY FIRE-FIGHTERS

The growth of parish and volunteer fire brigades during the nineteenth cen-tury saw several instances of brigades being formed entirely of females.

At Burton, Derbyshire, about twelve ladies con-stituted the strength of the Burton Ladies' Fire Brigade. They were equipped around 1900 with a manual pump and lowering lines, and wore ankle-length black skirts beneath a male-style brass-buttoned fire tunic. Frequent drill sessions were staged when the ladies would practise their skills, often before an appreciative audience. What the firemen of the town brigade thought of all this is not recorded.

Another ladies' fire brigade was that formed in the 1860s at Girton College, Cambridge. This group, drawn from undergraduates and college staff, relied upon equipment of a life-saving nature rather than fire-fighting kit. The ladies manned escape ladders and lowering lines and were drilled at regular intervals. Unlike the ladies of Burton, they were not provided with uniforms.

for a central grant to finance improvements in the local fire-fighting services. This grant was as much as 75 per cent of the cost of improvements, and included the cost of the recruitment and training of a volunteer force to be known as the Auxiliary Fire Service (AFS), to supplement the regular brigades in the event of war.

Later in 1938 came the Fire Brigade Act, which embodied many of the recommendations of a committee set up in 1935 under Lord Riverdale. This committee's brief was 'to review fire brigade services in England and Wales and to advise whether any steps are needed to improve organisation and co-operation for the purpose of meeting danger from fire'. The Riverdale enquiry led to a section of the Fire Brigade Act which, for the very first time, placed a statutory requirement upon the various county councils and other smaller local auth-orities to maintain *efficient* fire brigades. Interestingly, this latter act did not materially affect the London Fire Brigade, whose constitution and legal duties were little altered by the new legislation which in reality was framed around the statutory responsibilities of Massey Shaw's newly founded Metropolitan Fire Brigade of 1865.

The broad aim of the Auxiliary Fire Service recruit-ment was to provide enough firemen 'reservists' by the end of 1938 at least to supplement the professional crews in a positive manner in the event of hostilities. In the case of London, the target was 28,000 operational auxiliary firemen and several thousand women, whose primary role was intended to be that of communication and administration. By comparison, the peacetime strength of the regular London Brigade was 2,500 officers and firemen, based on 57 fire stations. The London auxili-aries would be expected to man 360 'sub-stations' and be virtually self-sufficient in the event of war. The recruiting concept called for two types of recruit: those who in the event of war would be prepared to become full-time firemen, and those who preferred to remain part-time auxiliaries.

Auxiliaries were enrolled in various categories ac-cording to medical and physical suitability, ranging from men in Class B – general fire-fighting duties – through Class B1 which was officially described as 'modified fire-fighting duty' and meant work at ground level only, to men in Class B2 fit only to man emergency fireboats of the river service. Women auxiliaries were initially placed in two grades, being suitable either for driving duties or for telephone and office work. Youths between fourteen and eighteen years old were earmarked for messenger and patrol duties, either on foot or by bicycle.

The national response to the Auxiliary Fire Service campaign was extremely disappointing number-wise, although enough men had come forward in most cities and larger towns for training to get under way by the end

of April 1938. This consisted of sixty hours' practical drill and theoretical instruction on such matters as hose running, use of pumps, ladders, methods of rescue, knots and lines, and salvage work. These sessions were conducted on regular fire stations at weekends and evenings, using professional firemen as instructors. Once qualified, an auxiliary attended weekly drill sessions. Women too had started their training by June 1938. Auxiliary officers were drawn from those recruits who had a professional background such as banking or the law. This was to cause some difficulty as the auxiliary service slowly grew in numbers during the autumn of 1938. In London, a number of experienced senior and middle-ranking regular officers resented the organisational responsibility given to the new 'untried' officers, and it was not until the coming of the first blitz raids in 1940 that the two forces found any proper sense of unity.

At the Auxiliary Fire Service training centres the volunteers were being trained on the numerous types of pumping appliance that they would use in the event of hostility. These included two types of self-contained fire engine, not unlike the pattern of the regular 'red' machines. Most were based upon Fordson chassis, with

Women were recruited into the Auxiliary Fire Service primarily for communications duties. Although they never took part in active fire-fighting, they did however man fuel carriers, canteen vans and later on became despatch riders. Here AFS firewomen are shown basic hose and hydrant drill. Lambeth Headquarters, 12 June 1940 (London Fire Brigade)

47

A London taxicab towing unit with trailer pump – the basic fire-fighting unit of the London Auxiliary Fire Service during the first two years of war. Note rolled hose lengths in luggage compartment and fare meter still in place. Lambeth, September 1939 (London Fire Brigade)

a Sulzer pump able to deliver 900gal (4,050 litres) per minute; a heavier Ford/Leyland unit had a maximum pumping capacity of 1,400gpm (6,300 litres) – enough output to supply six powerful jets of water. All the emergency fire engines were finished in battleship grey and were completely shorn of the normal splendid brass and chromium adornments of the regular 'red' machines. There were also four types of trailer-pump designed for towing behind suitable vehicles such as a light van or family-size saloon. These trailer-pumps had a pumping range of between 120 and 900gal (540 and 4,050 litres) per minute and were manufactured by several companies including Coventry Climax, Worthington Simpson, Dennis and Scammel.

All emergency equipment was provided direct to brigades from the Home Office. It was delivered in a steady stream from mid-1938 onwards and in addition to the pumping units and trailer-pumps came a great quantity of other fire-fighting equipment and stores, including many miles of 2½in (63mm) diameter hose. Most of the hose was American in origin and came in 50ft (15m) lengths, unlike the London Fire Brigade's 75ft (23m) hose. An immediate problem with the imported hose was its couplings; it utilised the male-female push-in type instantaneous connection while the LFB hose all had screw-type couplings. The incompatibility of these couplings necessitated the issue of suitable adaptors to all pumps to allow hose lengths to be interchanged. (Each LFB and AFS fireman carried a hose-spanner as part of his personal fire kit.)

There were, however, enormous logistical problems, particularly in London and the South East. There was, for instance, a chronic shortage of fire uniforms for the auxiliaries, many of whom in early 1939 had still only been issued with overalls, cap and rubber boots. Locating enough suitable buildings to requisition for fire stations in wartime was also an immensely difficult task. In addition, the installation of communications links between the AFS sub-stations and their parent regular fire stations seemed at times to take an eternity. Yet despite the deficiencies, the auxiliaries' morale was still high. Their numbers had been markedly boosted by the Munich crisis of September 1938.

Activity in the fire service continued apace as the situation in Europe deteriorated, reaching something of a climax in the latter weeks of August 1939. By this time detailed instructions on the establishment of sub-stations and their AFS fire-engines had been promulgated by the Home Office; 25 August was the last day for 'passing-out' AFS recruits after their sixty hours of basic training. Five days later steel helmets and respirators were issued to both LFB and AFS personnel and sandbag-filling and protection commenced at all London fire stations.

On 1 September 1939, the day that Hitler's troops invaded Poland, the final moves took place to put the fire service on an established war footing. Most regular city brigade personnel were recalled from leave and were instructed to remain on continuous duty at their stations. In London, all earmarked vehicles and river vessels were placed in commission at action stations and many premises yet to be officially requisitioned were taken over.

Then, at 5.20pm, a telegram arrived at London's Lambeth headquarters from the Home Office which cryptically stated: 'Emergency Fire Brigade measures. Call out AFS and proceed as in Home Office Circular 23/3/39.' Immediate steps were taken to bring the 23,000 erstwhile part-timers of London into full readiness in the front-line fire defence of the capital. Other brigades received similar messages. Thus, as Neville Chamberlain broadcast to the nation at 11.15am on 3 September 1939 and announced a state of war with Germany, the fire service braced itself for the onslaught of fire from the skies. Dramatically, just as Chamberlain finished speaking, the first air-raid warning sounded over London. The adrenalin of all firemen and firewomen must have surged, but the raid was not to be – after thirty minutes came the 'all clear'. This first warning was a result of a French aircraft arriving at Croydon aerodrome and causing jitters among some well-intentioned observers.

TAXIS GO TO WAR

An interesting fact about the AFS trailer pumps is that they came with no towing vehicle, and brigades were expected to utilise what transport they could for this purpose. Although the London Fire Brigade had already purchased sixty Fordson towing vehicles in order that the auxiliaries might perform drills with the trailer pumps, a number of Fordson light vans were also commissioned for the purpose of women's driving instruction. However, it was the London taxi-cab which proved to be the short-term answer to the trailer-pump problem.

In September 1938 the taxi-cab committee of the Transport and General Workers Union wrote to the Home Secretary, Herbert Morrison, suggesting that a taxi-cab might well be the ideal towing vehicle for fire service use, and so it proved. Strongly constructed, with a small turning circle and well able to carry a fair amount of hose, a short ladder and other fire-fighting equipment, over 2,000 cabs were 'hired' by the London Fire Brigade before the outbreak of war. In many cases an agreement was entered into to 'hire' taxi drivers as well, each thus becoming a part-time member of the AFS.

Leonard Rosoman

The wailing of these first sirens marked the beginning of the firemen's war; it was to be a long and arduous struggle against great odds. However, after a week had passed, it became clear that there was not going to be the threatened lightning strike by the Luftwaffe. As a result a shift-duty system was reinstated, and there took place much valuable training and consolidation of the AFS, their accommodation and equipment. At the end of the first week of war, there had been no fewer than 2,700 additional men and women recruits to the London AFS alone, whose strength was now close to the 25,000 originally envisaged. By Christmas 1939, recruiting into the AFS was stopped, as the system was at breaking point. And still there were no raids to test the auxiliaries, who in general were not even allowed to gain valuable experience at peacetime fires.

As 1940 came, the AFS's earlier high morale showed distinct signs of sinking and men and women started to resign, until a Statutory Order prohibited such losses. The lack of operational action, the low standard of accommodation and, in some cases, the 'amateur' status, all had their effect. In London, auxiliaries coined a new term for the lack of fire experience – 'Sitzkrieg'! Even the public's perception of the AFS started to be of men who were the 'darts-and-snooker brigade' or 'army dodgers'.

Even as these rumblings of discontent were growing,

War Artist Supreme. Royal Academician Leonard Rosoman's 'Wall falling on two firemen, 1940' painted whilst the young artist was a serving London auxiliary fireman. This superb painting graphically captures the horrific moment that every fireman dreads (Imperial War Museum)

King George VI pays a visit to London Fire Brigade's Lambeth Headquarters, during the early part of the Blitz period and is here inspecting the massed ranks of firemen despatch riders. During much of the war, operational messages were passed by motorcycle. 14 September 1940 (London Fire Brigade)

The fireboat Massey Shaw *returns to its native Thames after its part in the Dunkirk evacuation where the craft made three return Channel trips and did much ferrying off the beaches. Some of its firemen crew brandish .303 rifles. Note the knotted climbing aboard lines still lashed to the fireboat's sides. 3 June 1940* (London Fire Brigade)

A hose-laying lorry blown by bomb blast onto the roof of a three-storey terraced house, Bonar Road, Peckham, South London. It was several days before the vehicle was located buried in the debris of the badly blitzed area and some distance from where the bomb had fallen. No trace of its fireman driver was ever found (Daily Mirror)

so the real war was coming closer to the home front. As the early drama of Dunkirk began to unfold, the Admiralty requested that a fireboat be despatched to Ramsgate to protect the many petrol-engined vessels milling around the port. Within several hours, London's newest fireboat, the *Massey Shaw*, was on her way from her normal berth on the Thames at Blackfriars. But when the craft arrived next morning at Ramsgate, she with her crew of firemen was ordered to proceed across the Channel to Dunkirk. *Massey Shaw* was 78ft (24m) long yet drew only 3ft 9in (1.1m) in draft and, having been designed for fire-fighting in the Thames, she was not a sea-going vessel. Her men armed with no more than .303 rifles, *Massey Shaw* eventually made three round trips to Dunkirk over the next three days, as well as ferrying hundreds of waiting troops from the beaches to the larger naval and other ships. The London fireboat and her crew rescued in all around 700 troops and, unscathed apart from what was officially described as 'collision damage', she returned to a hero's welcome.

There then followed another lull before the storm of war broke over south-eastern England and, soon afterwards, London. Air-raid warnings wailed out with increasing urgency during August 1940 as the Battle of Britain raged overhead. On the night of 24 August, the Luftwaffe raided the fuel-tank installation at Thameshaven

in Essex with some effect, completely overwhelming the local brigade. Whilst most bombs, both explosive and incendiary, fell on their targets, several aircraft carried on up the line of the Thames to discharge their deadly loads over the City of London, where the incendiaries started many inaccessible fires high up on warehouse, office and church roofs around Fore Street and Cripplegate. The high explosives cratered roads, brought down buildings like collapsing packs of cards and caused water from broken mains to spout viciously upwards. Within twenty minutes of the raid starting, 200 pumps and 1,000 firemen were at work, many of them AFS personnel experiencing for the first time the real taste of smoke and flame. Elsewhere, in the West India Docks, 100 pumps and 2 fireboats were in the front line, while in east London there were 2 major fires burning, requiring over 50 pumps and 250 fire-fighters. And all this was the result of only a few aircraft.

Worse, much worse was to follow. After more raids on Thameshaven, where some London Fire Brigade convoy support was provided, the fearsome attention of the Luftwaffe was now to be permanently concentrated on London. Field Marshal Hermann Goering had directed that the capital city was to be bombed and burnt to the ground. Thus, from the night of 7 September 1940, German bombers relentlessly raided London and its

View looking along Whitecross Street, London, EC1, the morning after the very intense raid on the City area. The remains of burnt-out and bombed fire pumps litter the street from where thirty firemen were forced to abandon their appliances and retreat to safety. 30 December 1940
(London Fire Brigade)

suburbs for fifty-seven consecutive nights. It was a time that tested every fire-fighter, both regular and auxiliary, but the unified force very quickly joined to face the worst pyrotechnic bombing ever experienced in the modern world. While all others took shelter, firemen struggled – even as the bombs still fell – to get water jets to work to save buildings and nightly to prevent the situation developing into uncontrolled fire storms.

Often, warehouse fires posed additional problems because of their contents. At one inferno in Bermondsey the air was heavy with pepper, and firemen found breathing an unpleasant and difficult task in itself. There were paint fires, sugar fires and tea fires. At a dockside building full of grain, rats poured out in a steady stream to escape the fire and thick smoke inside. Fires in tar works and candle factories caused the liquid product to

DANGERS OF THE BLITZ

Two separate incidents of the London blitz illustrate the harsh reality of fire-fighting in the face of falling bombs.

The first took place during the initial raid of 7 September 1940. Whilst a fire was in progress in Peckham, South London, a high explosive bomb fell in Bonar Road, right under the tailboard of a London Fire Brigade hose-laying lorry which had been parked well clear of operations. The lorry and its driver literally disappeared.

Some three days later, when a lull in raiding permitted repair work to be carried out to the damaged terraced houses in the vicinity, a repair party found some hose amid the debris of a partially-collapsed house. Peckham fire station was informed and a crew went to the scene to attempt to retrieve the hose. When they arrived and scouted around the building, they found not only more hose under the bricks and timber but the missing hose lorry itself, firmly embedded in the roof structure and upper floor of the house. It was in a position where it was completely concealed from view from the street. The vehicle was remarkably intact considering that it had been projected over 100 feet through the air by bomb blast. Most of the hose that had been carried by the lorry was subsequently recovered, but no trace was ever found of the AFS driver.

The second incident, on 18 September 1940, involved the two-man crew of a turntable ladder which was at work as a water tower projecting a water jet onto a range of roof fires in Great Portland Street, W.1. The ladder was fully extended to 100 foot and the fireman at the top was about to secure himself to the ladder by a safety belt when a bomb whistled down past him and blew up in the street directly below. Here the second fireman was operating the ladder controls, and he, together with an officer standing close by, were severely wounded, the latter dying later that night.

But the fireman at the ladder top had an amazing escape from death. When the bomb burst, the chassis of the turntable ladder was blown sideways into the front of the building but the rear wheel, axle and ladder base section, collectively weighing over four tons, was projected right over the rooftops and came crashing to rest on another roof nearby. Various steel sections of the ladder were thrown onto the roof also, but the very uppermost ladder extension caught on a projection, turned over through 360 degrees and then hung back down over the face of the building, which was still on fire.

The unfortunate fireman who had been at the top of the ladder was thrown into the air and then plummetted to the pavement and was buried by falling debris. When the dust had settled a search was mounted in the area, and amongst the other casualties this fireman was found still alive but very seriously injured. After months in hospital he survived, and although disabled, was able to run a public house in Kings Cross, not far from the scene of his most incredible escape.

GALLANTRY

A singular act of fire service blitz bravery occured on 17 September 1940. Auxiliary Fireman Harry Errington was on duty at Rathbone Street sub-station, W.1., just off Oxford Street, when the premises were demolished by a direct hit.

Seven AFS personnel were killed outright but three others, including Errington, were injured and trapped in the basement. Fire broke out in the debris beneath which the other two firemen were trapped. Despite his own injuries, Errington extricated both men and carried them out to safety.

For his extreme courage, Errington was awarded the George Cross.

flow into the drains where it promptly solidified, resulting in further complications.

And through all this drama, excitement and danger, the AFS crews now found themselves hailed as heroes, and fêted as such by the community at large. By the end of the first week of London's continuous raids, 2 officers, 19 firemen and 1 woman auxiliary had been killed; 31 regular LFB men and 120 men auxiliaries had been seriously wounded; 11 auxiliaries were missing, presumed dead. Already 21 fire stations were amongst the bomb-damaged buildings.

And so it went on until the first respite from the continuous blitz came to the capital's fire-fighters on 3 November 1940. From then on, the Luftwaffe raided the provincial cities and ports, interspersed with regular return visits to London. Coventry, Birmingham, Southampton and other cities suffered heavy raids, and neighbouring fire brigades came into the affected area to supplement local fire-fighting efforts.

But such moves were not without their difficulties. Much equipment was not interchangeable between brigades, while senior officers leading reinforcing convoys to support another brigade's district would be unsure of retaining control of their own firemen. It was all rather haphazard, and by the time that the final huge fire raids of March and April 1941 upon London had been withstood, some very firm fire service and political

lobbying of the Home Secretary, Herbert Morrison, had taken place. The outcome was the National Fire Service (NFS), in which all 1,600 fire brigades in the United Kingdom came under one unified command on 18 August 1941. Under this scheme, the entire country was divided into regions, and then further into fire forces. For the first time, regular firemen and auxiliaries alike came under one common umbrella organisation. Although sporadic raiding still took place over London, the South East and other provincial areas of strategic importance, the NFS was able to build a firm foundation of standardisation in equipment, uniform, communications, rank structure and training. During the 'Baedeker' fire raids of April–June 1942, the NFS inter-regional convoy support worked well without any of the problems of the earlier blitz period.

Ironically, the NFS was never to be really tested by fire, although by 1944 its numbers nationally were around 42,000 firemen and women. Nevertheless, the regions covering the South East were to be stretched to the limit by Hitler's new terror weapon, the V1, the first of which fell on Barking in Essex on 13 June 1944. This new weapon was a petrol-injection ram-jet flying bomb, carrying 2,200lb (1,000kg) of high explosive at a terrifying speed of 350 miles (560km) an hour. The engine cut out shortly before the projectile fell and exploded on impact with the ground. The fall of this first V1 ushered in the period of most sustained activity in the life of the NFS in the London and South East region. Firemen attended every one of the incidents and dealt with many fires resulting from the explosion of these missiles. Fire did not always follow, however, and on such occasions fire service personnel, appliances and equipment were used to augment the Civil Defence and Ambulance Services in their task of coping with the large number of

THE JOB

'I can well remember the sight of Fireman Macawley (he's from Station 16) lying in the gutter with one of his legs off and the water from the fire running over his face, so that I thought he would be drowned . . .
Somehow the sight of a man you've known lying there with his leg off and the water running over him and nobody being able to do anything about it puts the wind up you. I have always thought that 'knees knocking together' was just a phrase, but my knees did literally knock together – I could feel them.

And then the Sub-Officer told me to get on up the ladder and put some water into the warehouse. So up I went and got on with the job.'
– Auxiliary Fireman Vic Flint, London Docks, 12 September 1940

casualties arising from the widespread blast effect.

Massed V1 attacks were experienced over much of southern England from June 1944 onwards, with a total of 638 flying bombs in that month alone. This meant an average of 12 per day of attack, the peak days of which were 16 and 18 June. As many as 1,121 V1s fell in July, and although the daily average then stood at 36, there were peak days on 2 July when 80 bombs fell, 6 July with 60, 22 July with 66 and 28 July with 57. This was in spite of an average of 30 V1s a day being brought down by RAF fighters.

Then on top of all this hectic activity of rescue and fire-fighting came an even more devastating and deadly weapon – the V2 rocket. The V2 carried a warhead of 1 ton (tonne) of high explosive, and the first of these giant missiles landed on Chiswick during the afternoon of 9

A WOMAN'S VIEW

'The control room is small. It has the width of a medium-wide passage. It contains four chairs, the control table on which stand the telephones, and a smaller table. On the walls there are boards and maps, on which discs are hung. The window is bricked up. The lights are harsh. The atmosphere is blue with the smoke, which cannot escape, of past hours. In fact, the control room disproves the theory that mammals require air in which to breathe.

There are two AFS girls and the mobilizing officer on duty. The telephones do not cease to ring, nor the slips, almost every one of which represents a fire, to be stabbed in order upon the file. I take my place. The girl whom I am relieving vanishes at once.

The mobilizing officer, speaking from behind me, says: "Send two pumps to John Mercer's premises, Goley Street, Thames Wharf." I transmit the order.

And so the night – very noisy – wears on. It may be that, in two more hours, every pump will have trickled back, all the fires under control. Or it may be that the drain of pumps from our station and from the five AFS sub-stations under us will not have been replaced by returning pumps, nor by reinforcing pumps from other areas whose drivers loom dramatically in the doorway with "Harrow" painted in white upon their steel helmets, or "Chipping Ongar" or "Slough".

On the night of which I am thinking, all our pumps were out and there were simply no more to despatch. This situation led to a lull in the control room but not in the raid.

The hours passed. No pump returned. A glance at the board would show you where they were: "Location of Fire", said the neat lettering, after which the address was written in chalk. In due course the other AFS girl was prodded awake. I took her place upon the bed, wrapping myself in my blanket. I felt like a soldier, but I did not sleep, not having the courage which would enable me to do so while that heavy droning filled the sky. This sound died from the heavens at last. I heard the telephone ring. I heard the message given to all sub-stations: "Air raid message White". Then came the long, high, certain, sweet note of the "all-clear".

At seven o'clock, as I went off duty, no pump had yet returned. The darkness of the street, after the glare of the control room, seemed for a moment like a wall against which one would strike oneself. The sky in the east was a bitter red which might have been the dawn but wasn't. Our pumps would be there, no doubt, frozen and soaking wet.

I felt the wind that cut at my face and hands. I felt the longing for sleep to which, so soon, I could yield; and to which the men at the pumps couldn't yield – perhaps, for hours. I felt delight that the perils of the night were at an end. And most of all, I felt – as I still feel – pride at being connected, however lightly, with so proud a service.'

Auxiliary Firewoman Outram after a night duty in an inner London control room, 1941

September, the violence of its explosion heard and felt many miles away. Unlike the flying bomb which gave long warning of its approach, the first intimation of the arrival of a rocket was its tremendous explosion and blast. From the beginning of September onwards the V2 rockets arrived with some consistency, working up from a total of 15 that month and 25 in October, to a peak of 116 in February 1945 and 115 in March.

By the end of the war in Europe on 8 May 1945, a grand total of 2,381 V1 flying bombs and 511 V2 rockets had fallen on the area covered by the London region of the NFS. At 900 of these incidents fires had been caused, and on every occasion there had been severe loss of life and damage. In the London region alone, fire-fighters had answered over 50,000 calls to fires and bomb explosions during the period August 1940 to March 1945. During the course of these historic operations, 327 firemen and women were killed, and over 3,000 seriously injured. But although the fire defence of the capital had occasionally faltered and at times been near to physical collapse due to sheer continuity of nightly raiding during 1940–1, the thin red line held and undoubtedly prevented London from suffering a fiery fate far worse than that of the 1666 conflagration.

REMEMBRANCE

327 London firemen and firewomen had died during enemy action between 1940 and 1945, recalled Winston Churchill, during a speech in the House of Commons at the end of the war.

He said: 'They were a grand lot and their work must never be forgotten.'

(Overleaf) *The new weapon of war arrives. View showing the scene very soon after a V1 flying bomb (or 'doodlebug') has fallen. Firemen, police and civil defence teams begin a careful seach and rescue operation. Middlesex Street, London, E1. 10 November 1944 (London Fire Brigade)*

HUMOUR AND THE FLYING BOMBS

There were times, even after a V1 raid, when amid the wreckage there was cause for a smile, as some firemen found when they tried to persuade a woman down a ladder from the first floor.

'But I can't come down,' she said tearfully. 'Not until I find my teeth!'

On another occasion, in a partially demolished house, firemen in the course of their search came upon a still recumbent figure of a man in bed. They removed the scattering of plaster from him, and had in their minds already recorded the man as being dead, when he sat up.

'Here! what's all this? What's going on here?' he demanded with all the petulance of one disturbed in his sleep.

At the scene of another V1 incident a dog was heard whining on a first floor. A fireman ran up a ladder and found the dog in a corner of a shattered room. Carefully, he lifted the dog and brought it down the ladder and set it on the ground. Immediately the dog made straight back for the ladder, scrambled up it, and disappeared into the corner from which it had been rescued.

At an incident where the front of a house had been torn away, firemen's torches lit up the ruins. From an exposed bedstead came an angry voice:

'Take your bloody lights away. I want to get dressed!'

After a V1 had fallen on Putney General Hospital a fireman saw through the debris the head and shoulders of a woman. He called his crew over and they started carefully to move the debris. After half an hour of lifting masonry and beams, one fireman was eventually able to touch the woman; she was quite cold and there was no obvious sign of life in her.

They worked on, and as they reverently removed the rubble from around her, it was discovered that she was naked. Another few minutes and she was freed: a life-size anatomical model made of rubber and plastic.

4 FROM BIG BRIGADES TO PARISH PUMPS

The de-nationalisation of the National Fire Service on 1 April 1948 saw the return of fire brigades to local authority control. However, instead of some 1,600 individual pre-war brigades, large and small, 150-odd fire brigades were now constituted. These ranged from the largest force in the country – London – to quite a number of small county borough brigades which, as in pre-war days, in some instances still consisted of only one fire station housing several appliances.

County borough brigades such as Darlington and Wigan were both examples of post-war small single fire-station brigades. Each had a complement of between 50 and 100 professional firemen who manned several pumping appliances and other support specialist fire-fighting vehicles. The pride of service and efficiency of these brigades was extremely high, perhaps partly due to the firemen being a small élite team, and probably well-known personalities throughout the community of the county borough which they served. At the other end of the scale, London possessed even then an enormous

A drill display at the Southwark Headquarters of the London Fire Brigade, circa summer 1906. It was the practice to invite dignitaries to watch these regular drills, hence the group of boater-hatted gentlemen in the foreground and also centre of photograph. Note powerful jets from steam pump, and the then-new horsedrawn 85ft turntable ladder shown partly extended and elevated (left) (London Fire Brigade)

A typical external view of a Victorian inner-city professional fire station, in this case London Fire Brigade's Redcross Street, in the City of London. In 1905, when the picture was taken, three appliances were based there and here the crew of one, a 50ft wheeled escape, pose for the photographer. Note the station officer in charge of Redcross Street (far left), his dog, and the immaculately turned out grey horses and appliance. Above the first floor is the spartan family accommodation that was a feature of the fireman's continuous duty system at that time (London Fire Brigade)

LIGHT FIRE ENGINE FOR COUNTRY DISTRICTS.

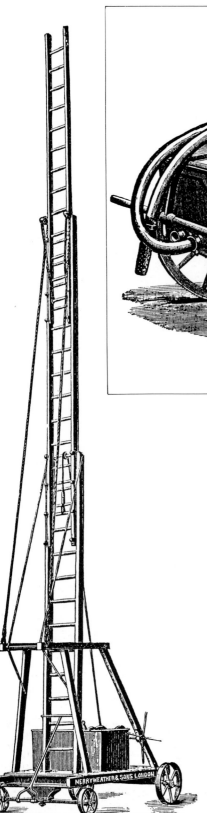

NEW PORTABLE FIRE ESCAPE FOR MANSIONS.

The growing risk of fire brought a stream of new life-preserving devices on to the market. Merryweather's portable fire escape for mansions was able to be extended to around third floor level (From The Fireman *journal, August 1884)*

Similarly, for rural volunteer brigades where both man and horse-power resources were uncertain, the Merryweather hand propelled manual fire pump would at least provide a reasonable fire-fighting jet, given that sufficient pond, lake or stream water was nearby (From The Fireman, *November 1884)*

brigade; indeed, it was one of the largest in the world. By the early fifties it consisted of 2,500 full-time officers and men who manned 241 fire-fighting appliances at 58 fire stations and 3 'floating' Thames fire stations, each with its own fireboat.

Since the end of World War II and a return to some normality on the home scene, emergency calls to the fire service had grown significantly right across the country, and nowhere more so than in the capital. By 1952, for instance, the London Fire Brigade responded to 20,328 individual calls to fires and other emergencies, representing a growth of some 15 per cent on 1948. The picture was much the same in the other big brigades such as Birmingham, Manchester, West Riding, Liverpool, Newcastle and Gateshead, and Glasgow.

In the early fifties, from its 20 fire stations, Birmingham's brigade of 650 men protected a population of over 1 million. The brigade ran 57 fire appliances of various types in order to provide cover to an area of 80sq miles

The equipment of a typical urban volunteer fire brigade – Acton, Middlesex, 1902. From left to right are: horse-drawn steamer, hose cart (foreground), hand-wheeled escape (background), horse-drawn manual, second hose cart, horse-drawn wheeled escape (London Fire Brigade)

Even as late as 1912 when this picture was taken, many sizable communities such as Cheam in Surrey relied on both volunteers and a single fairly primitive horsedrawn manual pump. The shield is, no doubt, for an inter-brigade drill competition of the time (London Fire Brigade)

A 1925 photograph of the Pen-y-bont (Bridgend) Fire Brigade in Glamorgan, South Wales. This was a part-professional brigade very typical of the period. Note the proud civic panoply as the Mayor, Town Clerk, clergy and the beadles pose with the smart and bemedalled firemen, a number of whom have seen active service in World War I (Author's collection)

FALSE ALARMS

Like most urban areas, Manchester had for some fifty years relied upon street fire alarms to provide a speedy method for the public to call out the brigade.

However, by 1958 street alarms had become very counter-productive, having been the route by which 898 malicious false alarms calls originated that year. One year later, all Manchester's 253 street fire alarms were decommissioned, the last city to take such action. Fortunately, genuine '999' calls could be made from the increased number of GPO telephone kiosks, although sadly this method still attracts the hoax caller.

(207km²) of Birmingham's inner city and suburbs. Interestingly, during the fifties Birmingham's brigade was also responsible for the city ambulance service. This joint arrangement was in force in several other authorities at this time, although over the next decade or so this duty was to be progressively relinquished by firemen as the operational pressures on fire-fighters continued to grow.

In 1950, Birmingham's firemen created new records as for the first time they answered over 5,000 emergency calls, although not all these came into fire stations by the '999' telephone system. Public fire-alarm call points were still a part of the urban domestic street scene across the country, and during 1950 other fire calls in Birmingham arrived by way of police telephone, automatic fire alarms in premises, and on no fewer than 478 occasions by a person physically dashing direct to the fire station to raise the alarm. In the same year, there were 19 fire deaths in the City of Birmingham area.

During this time, the trends in Manchester were much the same, with more actual fires (1,247) taking place than ever before, but with an unwelcome 27 per cent increase in malicious false alarm calls made by both street fire alarm and '999' system. The position in the smaller county borough brigades was, pro rata, much the same. As the decade moved on, there was an increase in the work-load of firemen dealing with emergencies other

than on the fire-fighting front. Non-fire rescue calls, such as the release of passengers trapped in road traffic accidents, steadily grew, as did the widest sort of dilemma involving children and animals, where the expertise and immediate response of the fire service were sought.

In 1948, at the time of the reconstituted post-war fire service, there still existed a small number of purely volunteer village fire brigades that fell outside the national framework setting up the re-formed individual brigades. Most of these small parish units had origins in the nineteenth century, when many owners of fine country houses purchased a manual or a steamer fire-engine to provide fire cover for the house and its estate. This self-provision for fire protection was in part the result of the great Victorian gentlemen's enthusiasm for fire-fighting. However, most such local rural volunteer brigades were progressively either absorbed by the new county brigades or were disbanded, as a brigade increased its own resources to meet the growing fire risks of its territory.

Alton in Hampshire is an example of an expanding community which in 1863 decided to abandon the existing ad hoc and unreliable arrangements for fire-fighting. In this year, a properly constituted volunteer fire brigade was formed, a manual fire-engine purchased for £160 and sufficient volunteers engaged so as to provide

Motorised fire engines are well established and developed in this 1920 view of London Fire Brigade's Shoreditch Fire Station in East London. Two pumps – LH8816 and XN498 – pose with pump escape LH8813. All three are immaculate petrol-driven Leylands of massive construction on solid-tyred chassis. Note that the fire bell has now become a standard warning device on London fire engines (London Fire Brigade)

A drawing of a typical open fire pump of 1934 vintage. This popular pattern of Dennis was made in large numbers for many UK brigades. It carried an inbuilt water tank which fed hose reel tubing as well as an extension ladder or (as in this case) a wheeled escape. Note also the twin amber flashing lights in front of windscreen (John Dobbs)

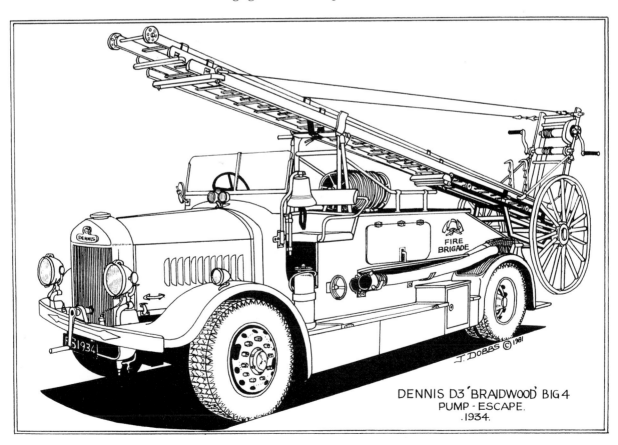

DENNIS D3 'BRAIDWOOD' BIG 4
PUMP-ESCAPE.
.1934.

A magnificent array of brass helmets and polished boots as King George VI inspects the ranks of London firemen before formally opening the new Lambeth Headquarters of London Fire Brigade. He is accompanied by the Chief Officer, Major Morris. The Queen is receiving a bouquet (far left). Note the band of the London Fire Brigade on bandstand (middle left) and the splendid array of fire engines. 21 July 1937 (London Fire Brigade)

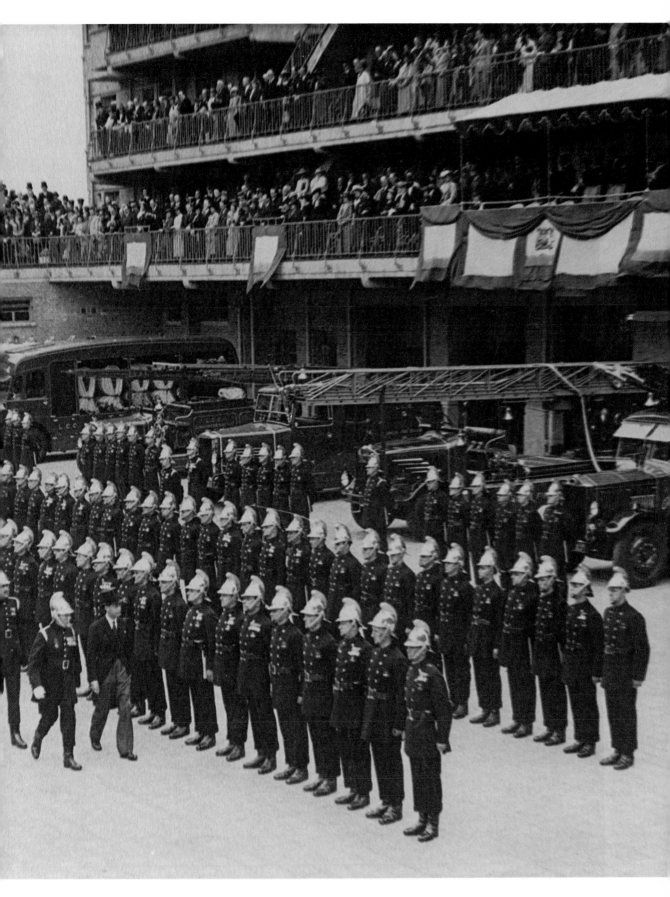

a guaranteed and speedy response to fires in the town. The costs of the new brigade were defrayed by public subscription. Interestingly, Alton's manual was supplemented in 1864 by a new Merryweather steamer, the first such engine to be commissioned outside the London area. Alton Volunteer Fire Brigade went on to provide ninety years of proud public service to the town before it became part of Hampshire Fire Brigade in the post-war era.

Between 1950 and 1974, several local government reorganisations took place, each having some effect on fire brigades. By the time of the major changes of 1974, which saw the birth of the present county structure, British brigades had been reduced to 67 large outfits. Apart from the London Fire Brigade, now with its 114 fire stations and 6,800 fire-fighters, each brigade had a combination of professional and retained (part-time) crews. In many senses, this preserved the best of the old parish brigades and yet provided the administrative and technical support of the large city establishments so necessary for the effectiveness of any fire brigade.

After the opening ceremony, the King and Queen watched a spectacular drill display and here the royal visitors' gaze is transfixed by firemen performing ladder drill some ninety feet up the new Lambeth drill tower. 21 July 1937 (London Fire Brigade)

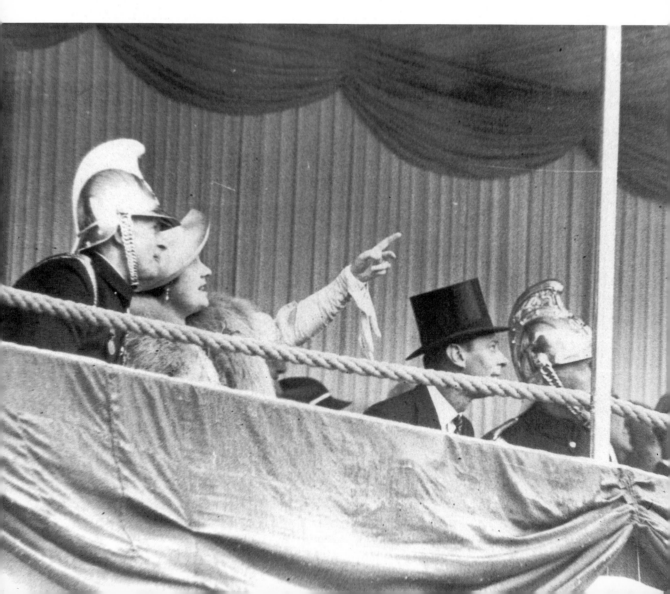

To all these past amalgamations of brigades, a steady and impressive national co-ordination has taken place in such matters as appliance design and manufacture, equipment compatibility, recruitment standards, training, promotion and uniform. The huge emphasis put on fire prevention and safety is also a product of recent years, and one can see that today's fire-fighter has come a very long way from the days of the Great Fire of 1666, of Braidwood's Tooley Street conflagration and of Massey Shaw's interminable struggles of a century past to set up a brigade fit for the capital.

> ### IN MEMORY OF . . . ONE OF MANY
>
> A juvenile, John Henry Steel, whilst searching for eggs in a barn on his father's farm, at Bolsterstone, Yorks., one day last month struck a match and fired the straw. His remains were found some hours later in a charred condition. The whole of the stables, cowhouses, and barns were damaged by the fire.
> – *Fire and Water*, October 1891

The end of street fire alarms. These red boxes were a feature of many towns and cities and in the late fifties had been around for forty years or so. However, the increasing use of the '999' system and the street fire alarms' vulnerability to vandalism and malicious use, led to their ultimate removal. Here one of Manchester's 253 fire alarms is being dismantled and taken out of service (R. F. Bonner)

5 FIRE-ENGINES OLD AND NEW

The forerunners of modern fire-engines can be traced as far back as the seventeenth century. During this period, a number of attempts were made to improve the capability of the most common fire-fighting device – the water squirt. By natural progression, the next step was to mount such squirts on wheeled chassis and provide them with a better built-in bucket-fed water supply from which a fire-fighting jet could be drawn without interruption to operations.

The Great Fire of 1666 undoubtedly concentrated the minds of the inventors of the time, but although several attempts were made to produce a mobile fire-engine which could provide a reliable water jet, it was not until 1721 that fire-engine design reached an important landmark. In this year, Richard Newsham, a London button manufacturer who had an interest in fire-engineering matters, was granted a patent for his design of a new and powerful manually pumped fire-engine. Newsham went on to produce various prototypes over

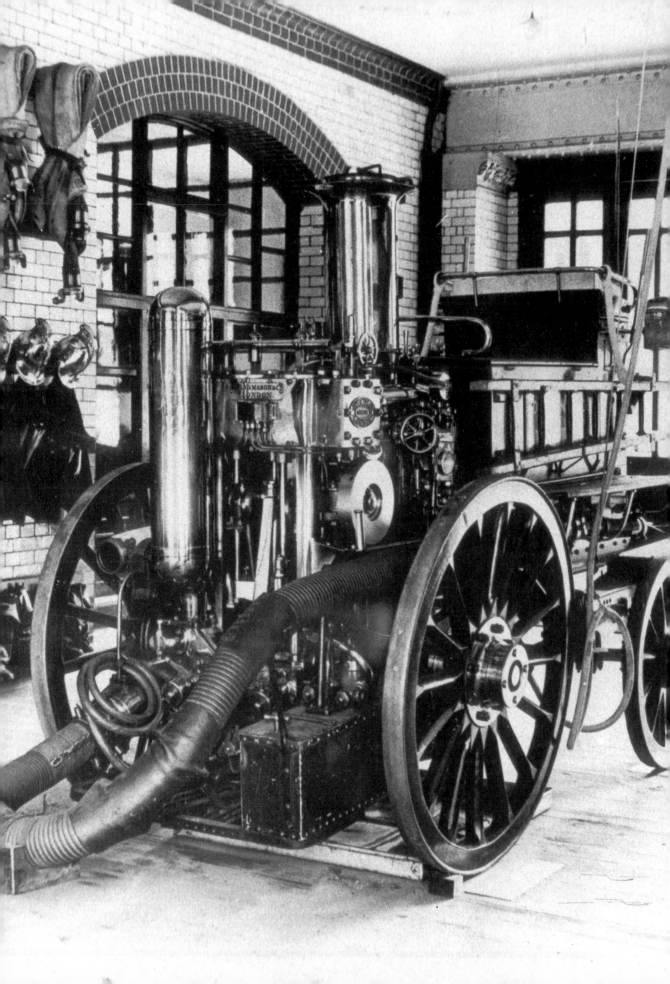

the next five years and developed a pump capable of projecting about 100gal (450 litres) of water per minute through a single nozzle. He perfected a clever system of valves within the body of the pump where the water supply was stored, which for the first time provided an uninterrupted jet. The pumping power was provided by large handles and treadles either side of the main body of the appliance.

By 1728, Newsham had abandoned his button business to concentrate on fire-engines, and he quickly became the acknowledged expert in his field, going on to market his pumps successfully in several overseas countries. Newsham's engines were, however, still manually hauled to the scene of a fire, but by the end of the century several horse-drawn manual pumps had been produced by the various manufacturers then engaged in fire-engine production.

Steam power was inevitably turned to fire-engine use early in the nineteenth century and in 1829 two London engineers, Braithwaite and Ericson, finalised the design of a horse-drawn steam pump, heralding a new age for fire-engine design. Subsequently, several companies devoted their production to the manufacture of steam fire-engines, notably Merryweather and Shand Mason, both London engineering concerns.

Surprisingly, steam power met with some resistance and it was to be several decades before steam-driven fire-pumps were accepted, in the early 1860s, as successors to the manually pumped fire engines of old. But manuals lingered on for another fifty years or so,

A London Fire Brigade Shand Mason horse-drawn steam pump of 1876 vintage still in operational use when this picture was taken some thirty years later. Steam at 100lbs pressure fed a two-cylinder 30 horsepower pump which provided 350 gallons of water per minute. The whole appliance weighed 1.5 tons and could be ready to pump six minutes after being lit up. Note row of uniforms and rolled hose above. Manchester Square Fire Station, London W1, 1906 (London Fire Brigade)

RAISING STEAM

When Shaw introduced the first steam-powered fire pumps into his brigade, they were drawn from the two principal British manufacturers, Merryweather and Shand Mason. The steamers were considerably more powerful than the earlier hand-operated pumps, and with a reliable water supply could throw a fire-fighting jet of water up to ninety feet in the air.

But unlike the manual pumps, the major difficulty with the steamers was ensuring that they had a head of steam by the time they arrived at the scene of the fire. Shaw carried out much development work and introduced a portable gas ring which was kept alight under a steamer's boiler whilst it was at the fire station. This device kept the temperature of the boiler water sufficiently high so that when a fire call came in, the fireman-engineer had time to ignite the ready-laid kindling inside the firebox whilst the horses were being speedily harnessed.

The fire was laid with kindling on top and a layer of best Welsh steam coal underneath. Once under way through the streets, the upward draught through the fire caused rapid combustion to take place and within several minutes sufficient heat was being drawn through the boiler tubes to lift the water temperature up a few degrees to boiling point.

Once at the fire, and by the time that hoses had been screwed together and a water supply to the fire engine obtained, steam would be singing from the safety-valve and the pump was ready for action. Simultaneously, the entire area would be blanketed by sparks and smoke not coming directly from the burning building but from the long polished brass chimney of the latest device which was, with some luck, going to put the fire out!

especially in the small brigades, both municipally run or of a voluntary nature. This was simply because a new steamer represented a considerable outlay, and the hand-pumped machines still formed a reasonable back-up to the powerful steamers.

In 1899, Merryweathers actually developed the first self-propelled fire-engine called the 'Fire King'. The boiler of the appliance fed steam to power either the rear wheels or the fire-pump, which was able to produce 400gal (1,820 litres) of water per minute. Although quite a number of 'Fire Kings' were sold, especially to the large brigades, they were slow and cumbersome, weighing some 5½ tons (tonnes).

However, by the beginning of the twentieth century the internal combustion engine was being applied to road vehicles other than cars. 1903 heralded the arrival of the first motorised fire-engine. This was built by Merryweathers for Tottenham Fire Brigade in north London, and within twelve months a number of other brigades had also taken delivery of similar pumps. Although there were several determined efforts to popularise both petrol-electric and battery-powered fire-engines, by 1910 the petrol fire-engine had virtually supplanted, as the fire-engine of the day, the steamer pumps of the Victorian age. The two principal manufacturers were Dennis Brothers of Guildford and Leyland's of Lancashire; both companies were to remain prominent suppliers for the next half-century and more.

In November 1921, the last horse-drawn appliance of the London Fire Brigade was withdrawn, an event not without expressions of sorrow. Many firemen who had grown up during the peak of the horse-drawn steam-pump era mourned the passing of a romantic age. Progress, however, was unrelenting, and although the first fully enclosed fire-engines, both of Dennis design, were introduced in the London and Edinburgh brigades in 1929, the majority of pumping fire-engines remained of an 'open' design right into the World War II period.

Around the turn of the nineteenth century, Merryweather's were keen to produce a self-propelled steam fire-engine and the result was their Fire King. *Weighing 5.5 tons it was capable of 25 mph and could pump 400 gallons per minute* (Portsmouth County Fire Brigade)

A horsedrawn tender of the London Salvage Corps. Salvage Corps were provided during the nineteenth century by a consortium of insurance companies in London, Liverpool and Glasgow to mitigate damage to business stock and fittings. The Salvage Corps took no part in firefighting but worked closely with firemen; the three Corps were disbanded in 1982 (London Fire Brigade)

A fine body of men. Nine firemen of Manchester Fire Brigade pose on their fire-engine outside Pollard Street Fire Station circa 1920. Each fireman is carrying an oval-handled key to open the covers of street hydrants. The Ford fire engine was a rarity in those days – note the rather frail construction and lack of front wheel brakes, as well as the left-hand drive (A. & B. Craven)

A view of the first ever purpose-built emergency tender, introduced by the London Fire Brigade in 1929. This vehicle, a Dennis, was pioneering for its enclosed body, then very rare in fire-engines. It carried a range of rescue equipment including Proto oxygen breathing apparatus, a primitive resuscitator, flame cutting gear, heavy jacks and portable lighting (London Fire Brigade)

Another early example of an all-enclosed fire-engine, a 1932 Dennis pumping appliance of Edinburgh Fire Brigade (London Fire Brigade)

A 1934 Dennis pump escape of the London Fire Brigade still had little weather protection for the crew. Quite a few firemen throughout the UK suffered serious injury and occasionally death when flung off en route to a fire (London Fire Brigade)

Another example of a 1930s style of fire-engine – a Bedford pump of Horsham Fire Brigade. Note midships mounted pump and spartan seating for the crew on the sides of the appliance (Author's collection)

By the start of World War II, many brigades were introducing all-enclosed appliances. Here is a 1938 Leyland of Croydon Fire Brigade which is beginning to take on the style of a modern-day fire-engine (John Dobbs)

A drawing of a classic fire-engine – a 1936 Leyland fitted with a 100ft steel mechanical turntable ladder, belonging to Croydon Fire Brigade. A number of these fire-engines gave thirty years sterling service including the 1940–41 Blitz period (John Dobbs)

This was rather surprising, as the journey to the scene of a fire was a very hazardous affair. En route to the emergency, each fireman would have to complete his dressing in his fire uniform. Hopefully, he would have pulled on his boots and waterproof leggings by the time the fire-station doors crashed open and the fire-engine lurched out onto the highway. But putting on his tunic and belt with axe was never easy, complicated by the appliance driver weaving through traffic and swinging the engines round corners at speed. Little wonder that the incidence of firemen being thrown off on the way to a fire was fairly common, usually with serious injuries to the victim. The widespread introduction therefore of enclosed crew cabs in the post-1939–45 period was a very welcome fire-engine design evolution.

Since then much emphasis has been directed towards the safety of the fire-engine crew, and all modern appliances are constructed to a national specification which demands powerful braking systems, rigid steel-framed body construction and low centres of gravity to provide stability at speed.

From the manual fire-pumps of Braidwood's days have thus emerged today's maid-of-all-work, the water tender. This fire-engine predominates in the fleet of all fire brigades and carries various ladders up to 45ft (14m), around 1,500ft (457m) of large diameter hose,

LEYLAND-METZ
100FT. TURNTABLE LADDER
500 G.P.M. INTEGRAL PUMP
1936.

LEYLAND SFKT2.
PUMP - 500 G.P.M.
1938.

Fortunately, the London Fire Brigade preserved several of its steamer pumps. Here, a well-polished 1876 Shand Mason is in use during a 1938 display at Lambeth Headquarters. The brass helmets are by 1938 purely ceremonial, and the fireman crouching is firing the steamer through a rather inaccessible firebox door (London Fire Brigade)

breathing apparatus, lighting and salvage equipment, cutting and lifting gear for road traffic and other accidents, resuscitators and chemical protection suits. In addition, the water tender has an inbuilt water tank of some 400gal (1,800 litres) capacity which, using the powerful on-board fire-pump and hose reel tubing, is capable of producing instant jets of water or water fog cooling sprays without first having to connect into street fire hydrants. Water tenders also have much additional equipment and are usually crewed by five or six fire-fighters.

As the work of the fire service has gradually diversified, particularly over the last seventy-five years, various specialist fire-engines have been developed. Today these include high-rise appliances – both turntable ladders and hydraulic platforms; emergency and rescue tenders, for accident crash work and spillages of hazardous materials; hose layers, to lay out hose to supplement existing water supplies at rural or major fires; and foam tenders, providers of large quantities of foam for large petroleum and fuel risks. In addition to this list of front-line vehicles there are various support appliances such as control and canteen units. Today the long-established British manufacturer Dennis still produces a fire-engine chassis as well as Dodge (now Renault), although an increasing trend in recent times on the British scene has also seen the arrival of

LONDON'S FIRE HORSES

Horses for pulling London's fire engines had been hired from various livery stables during Braidwood's years of command (1832–1861), but under Massey Shaw's subsequent direction, new arrangements were made.

In 1867, Shaw contracted with the horse-bus company of Thomas Tilling to supply specially bred horses for fire brigade use. These began to be delivered as very sturdy greys, about 15 to 16 hands. They needed to be strong, for the new steam fire pumps weighed about five tons (tonnes) with a crew of six firemen aboard. Tillings provided horses of about five years of age after they had undergone three months' special training for the job. This included being lead horses in a four horse bus plying through London's most densely populated areas between Peckham and Oxford Circus. Once in the brigade, a horse would work for about five years before being retired.

On fire stations, the horses would be the responsibility of the brigade coachmen and were very well cared for. They were housed in stalls in a yard immediately behind the fire engines so that they could be moved quickly to a position between the shafts when the fire alarm bell sounded. Each engine was pulled by a pair of horses. Special quick-fitting harnesses locked under the horses' necks, and the fire engine would be ready to move off well inside a minute of the call. Experienced horses would need no encouragement to respond to a call, and would quickly and with no fuss make their own way to the shafts.

Similarly, once at the fire the horses knew their drill. If it was only a small outbreak, the coachmen would leave them in the shafts, but if the fire was serious and spreading, the horses would be unharnessed and led away to a quiet corner, there to be fed on buns, fruit and sweets by an admiring crowd.

Airport firefighters of the BAA Gatwick Fire Service tackle a training fire of burning jet fuel using a powerful six-wheeled Nubian foam tender able to project a large quantity of foam onto the burning fuel. Note the fireman above the vehicle cab about to unleash the foam jet. Gatwick Airport, 1981 (West Sussex Fire Brigade)

COSTS

The cost of fire engines has risen enormously since the days of the manual pump. Around 1850, the cost of a typical four-man-a-side manual pump was £150. Contrast this sum with the cost today of a water tender, which depending on the sophistication required, can be between £70,000 and £80,000. This figure is simply for the fire engine only. Equipment, of which there is a large and diverse amount, can add thousands more to the cost.

Specialist appliances can be even more costly. A new turntable ladder or hydraulic platform can be priced from £200,000 upwards.

Mercedes, Volvo and Scania fire-engines.

Over its 150 years of fire-fighting and rescue, the service can demonstrate very progressive developments in fire-engine design for both rural and urban use. Providing the tools of the profession has been an integral part of fire-service history and is essential and complementary to the physical demands and danger that accompany the modern fire-fighter as he goes about his task.

A 45ft ladder-carrying Leyland Comet pump of Kent Fire Brigade. This 1953 fire-engine, then based at Beckenham Fire Station, had a petrol engine and two-speed rear axle which was rather unusual in fire appliance design (John Dobbs)

Another classic fire-engine. The 1950 Dennis F12 was acquired by many brigades up and down the country; that in the drawing is of Surrey Fire Brigade. Powered by a Rolls-Royce eight cylinder petrol engine, they were extremely successful and many lasted into the 1970s (John Dobbs)

A more modern 1975 Dennis pump escape of the London Fire Brigade, some of which are still in service. These fire engines have a turbo-charged diesel engine, automatic transmission and power steering. The traditional hand rung bell is still retained on this example (John Dobbs)

DENNIS F12 - ROLLS ROYCE B80 ᴍᴋ X.
PUMP
900 G.P.M.; 100 GALS WATER.
0-60 M.P.H. IN 45 SECONDS.
.1950.

LEYLAND COMET
PUMP - LADDER
45 FT. ALLOY LADDER , 500 G.P.M., 100 GALS. WATER.
.1953.

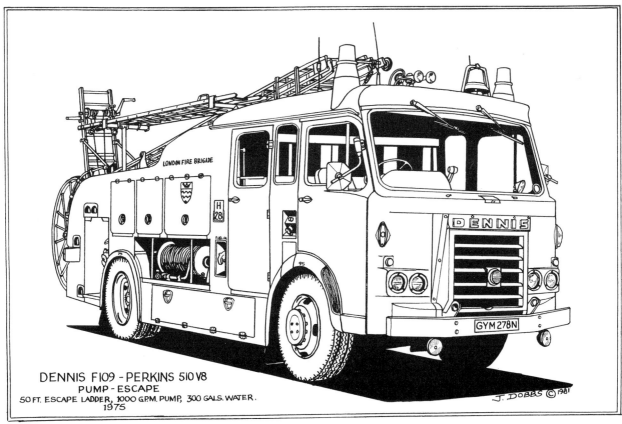

DENNIS F109 - PERKINS 510 V8
PUMP - ESCAPE
50 FT. ESCAPE LADDER, 1000 G.P.M. PUMP, 300 GALS. WATER.
1975

89

A 1988 series Dennis water tender of Devon Fire and Rescue Service is dwarfed by a British Airways' Concorde during a visit to Exeter Airport. May 1988 (Doug Smith)

Some of the weaponry of the modern fire-fighter seen here laid out in front of the various appliances of the Devon Fire and Rescue Training School at Plymouth. The appliance second from right is a 100ft hydraulically operated turntable ladder, whilst the other three fire-engines are maids-of-all-work water tenders – each carrying 400 gallons of water and almost ¼ mile of hose (Devon Fire and Rescue Service)

A 1988 series Dennis water tender of Devon Fire and Rescue Service poses with the RAF Red Arrows during their stopover at Exeter Airport. May 1988 (Doug Smith)

6 SOME FAMOUS FIRES

The Burning of the Crystal Palace

One of the capital's largest and most spectacular fires of the early twentieth century was the destruction of the Crystal Palace on Anerley Hill, south London, on the night of 30 November 1936. Paxton's vast showpiece building was originally constructed in Hyde Park to house the Great Exhibition of 1851. It was subsequently re-erected on Anerley Hill in 1854. The imposing glass, timber and cast-iron framed building was over ¼ mile (.4km) in length and at its widest part some 450ft (137m). The height of the transepts reached 200ft (61m), whilst the two flanking towers were each 250ft (76m) high. The building and its vast ornamental gardens actually lay within the Penge Urban District area which abutted the London County Council boundary along the main thoroughfare of Anerley Hill.

At about 1925 hours on the fateful night, a private fireman employed at the Crystal Palace saw a streak of flame run along the top of a room. Quite incredibly, considering the vast risk of the massive building, Penge Fire Brigade were not called until thirty-four minutes later. When they arrived with their total complement of one motor pumping appliance and eight firemen, a severe fire was raging inside the central glazed transept. Despite being hampered in their efforts by crowds of sightseers and motorists, Penge Fire Brigade managed to attack the spreading inferno with their entire resources – one jet of water.

The Penge firemen soon called for help and the London brigade quickly came to the aid of the totally overwhelmed local firemen. As the reinforcing pumps arrived and went into action it was clear that the fire had gained a considerable hold over the historic building, for a strong wind was fanning the flames. Only ten minutes after the Penge crew arrived, the entire centre transept collapsed in a spectacular and upwards-spiralling mushroom cloud, throwing up fragments of burning glass and timber sparks. In the words of one eye-witness, 'the building began to flame from end to end'.

A huge crowd gathered, hampering the efforts of every fresh fire-engine which tried to get to the scene. Even then, once the crews had fought their way through the jostling throng, an insufficient water supply added to the many fire-fighting problems. The whole of the Crystal

Palace area was soon ankle-deep in interwoven fire hoses, and within an hour of the arrival of the first Penge firemen more than 70 pumps and other appliances, crewed by over 400 fire-fighters, were at work. Command of operations was by now vested in the London Fire Brigade.

At this stage the fire could be seen from most of south and central London, and the glow was even clearly visible in all the surrounding counties. Among the dignitaries who visited the scene during the prolonged operations was the Duke of Kent who, accompanied by Major Morris, Chief Officer of the London Fire Brigade, moved through the wind-blown smoke, sparks and spray amongst the crouching firemen.

Slowly and remorselessly, the Crystal Palace which had been a landmark to Londoners for eighty-five years, twisted and fell to earth. By midnight the inferno had been surrounded on all sides by a barrage of jets and was under control. Fire-fighting carried on all through the night, and in the misty first light of dawn almost the entire 28 acre (11ha) site of the Palace contained only thousands of tons of blackened, smouldering piles of twisted ironwork and great solidified sheets of lava-like glass. Only the two towers survived, and they appeared even taller as they bore witness to the sad and wholesale destruction below. Whilst no members of the public lost

A 'morning after' view of all that is left of Paxton's 1851 glass and timber Crystal Palace after the huge fire the night before, 30 November 1936. Part of the east transept and tower remain although the latter was demolished just before the London Blitz began for fear of aiding the navigation of the Luftwaffe (London Fire Brigade)

A ROYAL VISITOR TO THE CRYSTAL PALACE FIRE

Shortly after the centre transept had collapsed, and the fire was beginning to die down, a very agitated messenger rushed up to say that the Duke of Kent had arrived at the fire and would like to see the Chief Officer. He had an equerry with him, and after we had had a look at the fire from the front, I asked him if he would like to have a walk round and see the engines at work from the lake, where the branches were continuing their rather hopeless task of trying to save the end of the north transept.

He had arrived in full evening dress from an official dinner, so I suggested that we lend him a helmet, top boots, and a mackintosh. He jumped at the idea, but I wanted if possible to take him round by himself, without his equerry; we could then get away from formalities, and it would be much easier to introduce the officers direct to him, as I felt sure he would prefer this. I therefore gave an officer the tip; 'One helmet and one pair of boots only. Say, that's all we can find.'

The ruse worked and off we went, leaving the equerry standing in evening dress on the dry road, while the Duke trudged along through all the water and mud that always collects round a large fire.

Well, we all had a

their lives in the blaze, several firemen required hospital treatment for cuts and burns.

At the subsequent inquiry it was thought that leaking gas had been the cause of the fire, and the delay of over half an hour between the discovery of a flame and the first alerting of the fire brigade allowed the fire to develop unhindered and to gain a considerable hold. The fire-spread was also aided by the vast open and unpartitioned areas of the transepts together with a lack of fire-protection equipment such as a sprinkler system. The absence of such fundamental fittings in a vast public building would not be allowed under today's stringent fire and building regulations.

At its second home on Anerley Hill, the Crystal Palace had survived several near disasters before the ultimate tragedy struck. In 1853, while re-erection work was in progress, a serious collapse of scaffolding killed twelve workmen. The north wing of the Palace suffered severe storm damage in 1861, and this same wing was destroyed by fire five years later, although on this occasion it appears that the local brigade were successful in containing the outbreak. In 1880, a large elevated water tank burst, causing considerable damage.

In its heyday in the late nineteenth century, the Crystal Palace hosted many exhibitions, concerts and fêtes, and the odd firework display. It was visited by royalty from many parts of the world, while Blondin, the high-wire walker, performed his amazing feats on a wire suspended between the ornate glazed panels of the central auditorium. And, somewhat ironically, selected contingents of various fire brigades were reviewed in July 1891 at the Crystal Palace by the Kaiser and the Prince of Wales, the entire parade being led by the recently retired Chief Officer of the Metropolitan Fire Brigade, Sir Eyre Massey Shaw, KCB.

The burning of the Crystal Palace brought to an end a structure that had enjoyed a glorious and spectacular history, and London would never see another similar glass, timber and iron building of such massive dimensions. The final pyrotechnic display as the Crystal Palace itself blazed is still remembered with awe by many South Londoners, who readily recall that windy, cold and dramatic November night fifty-three years ago.

Yet it wasn't quite the end of the Crystal Palace story. The two towers, one at each end of the vast iron and glass structure, and which for over eighty years had formed a landmark on the ridge of Anerley for those living many miles north and south, remained a gaunt reminder of a famous building and the dramatic night of its destruction. But in 1939, a new threat arrived. As the country braced itself for war, air force and military intelligence considered them too significant a landmark for the Luftwaffe, and both structures were demolished just before the outbreak of hostilities. Thus the towers,

View of one side of the LNER/ British Railways goods warehouse in Eldon Street, East London, after a huge £1 million fire had been eventually overcome the night before. During fire-fighting operations, the end wall of the entire top floor suddenly fell outwards, killing three firemen and seriously injuring twelve others. The photograph shows the widespread fall of brickwork and the damage inflicted to five wheeled escape ladders on which many of the casualties were working, as well as the adjacent buildings. 21 December 1951 (London Fire Brigade)

which were saved by the efforts of firemen, eventually fell as a result of fear of invasion by the forces of the Third Reich.

Perhaps this was as well, as during the London Blitz and the later raids by V1 flying bombs and V2 rockets, direct hits were regularly scored upon or very close to the site of the Crystal Palace. Had the Palace and its towers still been standing, they would have undoubtedly presented an enormous risk, both of fire and structural collapse.

Another Massive London Fire

At 1944 hours on the evening of 21 December 1951, two pumps from the Whitefriars Fire Station of the London Fire Brigade turned out to a fire in the old North London Railway (later BR) Broad Street Goods Depot, located in Eldon Street, EC2. These first crews were at the scene within three minutes and reinforcements were immediately requested. The three upper floors of the huge five-floor warehouse, full of general merchandise, were already well alight.

Seventy-five minutes later, two firemen were dead, a third lay dying and twelve others had been seriously injured when part of a wall suddenly crashed down onto Eldon Street, into the very heart of fire-fighting operations. The collapse also crushed two turntable ladders,

(continued)
splendid time with him, and I was able to introduce to him not only the Principal Officers and Superintendent, but what was of great moment to the Brigade, some of the young Station Officers who had been having a very thick time.

Like the other members of the Royal Family I have met in connection with my work, he took the keenest interest in all he saw, asked numerous questions that were always to the point, and I really believe he enjoyed his experience. Anyhow, it was a change from after-dinner speeches!

From the memoirs of Major C. B. Morris, CBE, MC

and virtually demolished three 50ft (15m) wooden-wheeled escape ladders, from which a number of firemen had been working water jets.

When the chief fire officer assumed command of the incident at 20.00 hours, there were no fewer than 100 pumps and 8 turntable ladders at work, crewed by 500 officers and men. At the height of the conflagration there were 41 jets of water at work, pumping some 9,000gal (40,500 litres) of water per minute into the flames. As with all serious City fires, at one stage there was a real threat of fire spreading further into the historic square mile, but this danger was eventually averted.

The fire burned for seven hours before coming under control, and firemen remained on the scene, damping down and clearing up for four days. The cause of the fire was never established.

Tragedies in Scotland

In 1960 a conflagration of appalling magnitude took place in Glasgow – a city inured to death and suffering caused by fire. When other cities in the United Kingdom were able to demolish slums and develop new areas of housing and industry, Glasgow still had a vast legacy of densely packed dwellings, workshops and warehouses which meant a fire-risk probably second to none. Indeed, men of the Glasgow Fire Brigade boasted that they were the busiest in the world, and it was certainly true that the loss of life and the incidence of serious outbreaks in the Scottish city were far higher than elsewhere.

In the early evening of 28 March, three fire appliances of Glasgow brigade were called to a fire in a bonded store full of whisky. The six-storey building in Cheapside Street was in an area of congested and narrow streets close by the Clyde and surrounded by other bonded stores and warehouses. When the first crews arrived at about 19.18 hours, there was considerable smoke and heat coming from within the bond, but no actual fire was showing from the building. Immediate reinforcements were called for and breathing apparatus crews began to penetrate the smoke-filled floors to locate the seat of the hidden fire. Additional hose jets were laid out ready to protect the surrounding premises should the fire in the whisky bond suddenly break loose. Then without any warning and some thirty minutes after the first '999' call, came the most deafening explosion from deep inside the building, instantly blowing out the front and rear walls and showering hundreds of tons of brickwork and debris out into the surrounding thoroughfares.

Once the clouds of dust has settled, there in side streets stood piles of rubble, some 15ft (6m) high, where firemen and their appliances had been at work only seconds earlier. The unleashed fire within the bond was now fed by many thousands of gallons of whisky and it

The aftermath of Cheapside Street, Glasgow, showing the crushed remains of a turntable ladder around which three of the fourteen firemen died. Note the whisky barrels and enormous extent of the building collapse into the street after the explosion. 29 March 1960 (Strathclyde Fire Brigade)

roared its ferocity at the firemen, the flames reaching high into the night sky. By the light of the inferno, surviving firemen tore with their bare hands at the piles of rubble under which many colleagues were trapped, but it quickly became apparent that no one underneath could still be alive.

More appliances raced to the scene, to try to check the advance of the fire which had now spread to two adjoining whisky bonds, a large bottling store and part of the roof of a shipbuilders. In the latter building, large quantities of liquid air lay stored, and there was a very real danger of a further massive explosion had the fire engulfed any more of the shipbuilders' premises. But the battle to contain the blaze was eventually won at about 01.30 hours the next morning, by which time over seventy fire-fighting jets were at full blast, including several from a Glasgow Fire Brigade fireboat pumping from the Clyde.

The explosion and fire in the whisky bond had devastated the building and it was only after the fire was under control that firemen began the sad task of recovering the bodies of their colleagues. Up to this point, the exact number of those missing was not known, although a roll-call was being taken. To everyone's horror, when the results of this became known there appeared to be nineteen men 'missing presumed dead'.

As the rumour of a disaster spread quickly around the city, the wives and relatives of firemen on duty that evening gathered at the fire station headquarters. As the crowd grew desperate for news, the scene was more like that found at the head of a mine shaft following an accident. No one knew exactly how many men were dead, and as the great fire burned on, the anxious groups waited for news that their loved ones were safe. In the near distance, clanging fire bells of appliances gave an urgent edge to the sad scene.

As dawn rose over the city and while crews were still at work damping down the smouldering remains of fire, the last of the bodies was recovered from under the rubble. Slowly, the scale of the tragedy became clear: the death total stood at 19 men. Of these, 14 were Glasgow firemen and 5 were members of the city's Salvage Corps. The bodies were so mutilated that identification was only possible through uniform numbers and items of personal belongings.

All the dead men except one were married, and most had young children. Their service ranged from that of a fireman only one year in the brigade, to the deputy chief salvage officer who had thirty years' experience to his credit.

That morning, the people of Glasgow went to work stunned by the disaster in Cheapside Street. Hundreds of messages of sympathy poured in, including one from the Queen. Later that day, Princess Margaret interrupted a civic visit to Glasgow to view the still-smoking remains of the ill-fated whisky bond and the surrounding damage. Even at this early stage, the fire loss was estimated to be around £5 million. The whole country mourned the awful loss of life, a total which still stands today as the worst single tragedy ever to befall the British Fire Service.

Several months later, the inquiry into the disaster heard that the explosion was likely to have been caused by a build-up of whisky vapour becoming ignited by flame within the bond itself. The fire was attributed either to a dropped cigarette end or match, or to an electrical fault. Recommendations were made at the hearing that an automatic fire alarm system should be installed in all bonded warehouses to give an early warning of smoke and fire, and that the siting of such bonds should in future be licensed.

The dedication to duty on the part of those concerned in that dreadful night did not go unrecognised. To quote from *The Fire Journal* of November 1960:

It is with pride and pleasure that this month we use the space normally occupied by our editorial to record the awards of two George Medals, three British Empire Medals and a Commendation to members of the Glasgow Fire Brigade for heroism during the disastrous whisky

A FIREMAN'S THOUGHTS

Eventually we came to a standstill at the dockside wharf where we were to spend this endless night. Everything seemed to be on fire in every direction, even some barrage balloons in the sky were exploding. The cinder-laden smoke which drifted all around us made one think of the destruction of Pompeii.
– *Auxiliary Fireman Peter Blackmore, Surrey Timber Docks, South London, 7 September 1940*

warehouse fire.

We are sure that these awards will be a tribute not only to the men concerned but also to the whole of the Glasgow Fire Brigade, to the memory of the nineteen who died, and indeed to the hazardous work carried out by fire-fighters every day throughout the country.

As if to underline the constant hazards faced by its fire-fighters, another tragic and major fire took place in Glasgow in August 1972. Seven firemen, all wearing breathing apparatus, were working inside a burning cash-and-carry warehouse when the roof collapsed and fell into the fiery interior. All seven men perished and in a House of Commons message of sympathy to relatives, Mr Gordon Campbell, Secretary of State for Scotland, said: 'This is a tragic reminder of the debt we all owe to men of such heroism who perform a public service we can never take for granted.'

The Summerland Disaster

The £2 million Summerland pleasure centre on the sea front at Douglas, Isle of Man, was the scene of an appalling fire disaster on 2 August 1973. The six-storey complex was built into a cliff-face and consisted of amusement halls, discothèque, bingo halls, restaurants and bars. Summerland covered 3½ acres (1.4ha), and the walls and roof were entirely clad with acrylic plastic sheeting. There were about 4,000 people in the complex at the time of the fire.

At about 20.00 hours, a passing taxi-driver noticed a

Horror on the Isle of Man. The Summerland complex at Douglas burns fiercely after a small deliberately lit fire has spread up the wall cladding quickly to envelop a large part of the leisure centre's structure. Forty-nine persons died in this inferno. 2 August 1973 (Noel Haworth)

small fire burning on the outside face of the building and radioed an alarm. Two pumps from nearby Douglas Fire Station turned out within two minutes and were very quickly on the scene. The crews were confronted with an awesome task. A severe and spreading fire had already taken hold of most of the building and dense clouds of black smoke poured skywards. Fire-fighters were hampered by the burning external plastic cladding but despite this they managed to carry out a number of rescues of men, women and children trapped inside and cut off by the flames.

It wasn't until about one hour later that the inferno was under some control, by which time all 16 fire-engines on the Isle of Man and 93 firemen were at the scene. But as the first bodies were recovered, it rapidly

Why? An Isle of Man fireman pauses for reflection during the massive clearing up exercise after the Summerland fire tragedy. Note how some of the rustic wooden staircase is scorched by radiated heat from the intense fire in the main building nearby. 2 August 1973 (Press Association)

SOME FAMOUS FIRES

A bolt from the blue. The roof of the South Transept of York Minster burns dramatically, following a severe electric storm believed to have caused the fire. 9 July 1984 (Bettison/Cheetham)

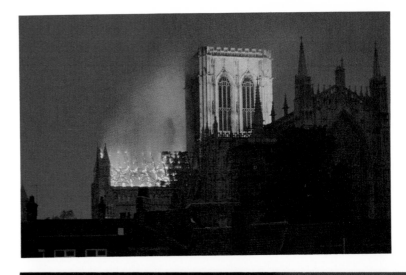

A dramatic view of fire sweeping through the top three floors of Dingles department store, Royal Parade, Plymouth, on the evening of 19 December 1988. Note turntable ladders at work and hose lines going up face of building on left. Far blue light on left is the Devon brigade's control unit which is coordinating the efforts of 150 fire-fighters, many of whom are inside Dingles in breathing apparatus at this time. Arson is thought to be the likely cause of this huge fire, one of the largest in the UK during that year (Marc Hill)

became clear that here was a disaster of momentous proportions. Many casualties were located at the foot of the main staircase of the complex, and before long the death toll had risen to forty-nine.

The subsequent public inquiry found that the fire had been caused by a youth setting fire to a dismantled fibreglass kiosk. The fire spread to an accumulation of rubbish and from there to the plastic cladding material which contributed to the rapid spread of fire up the external walls, and to the early collapse inwards of the roof complex. Never again was such man-made material to be used in the manner it had been at Summerland – a name that meant death and suffering to so many families on that fateful August day.

7 TRANSPORT FIRES

RAILWAYS

The history of the railways over 150 years and more is regularly punctuated by serious accidents of one sort or another. Although fires involving rolling-stock have occurred only infrequently over the years, they have tended to incur very tragic outcomes, as the following incidents show.

Hawes Junction – First Major Fire

On a rainy Christmas Eve, 1910, an early morning collision took place north of Hawes Junction on the Midland Railway's Settle and Carlisle route to Scotland. The crash happened when a signalman at Hawes Junction, working under pressure at a time of intense traffic, forgot that two locomotives coupled together were waiting for a suitable gap in the northbound stream of trains to return home to Carlisle. The signalman pulled his signals off for a northbound sleeping-car express and unwittingly allowed the two waiting locomotives to pull

Early fire-fighting measures on the Thames circa 1870. The fire tug Antelope *with its float move into position in tackling a warehouse fire. On the float is mounted the steam fire pump which at maximum power lifted about two tons of water per minute from the river – enough to feed about eight effective jets of water* (London Fire Brigade)

away towards their destination. They had proceeded only about 2 miles (3km) into the swirling rain when the sleeping-car express, travelling almost three times as fast, rammed the rearmost of the two locomotives.

All the carriages of the express were derailed. They piled into each other and toppled over against the edges of a deep cutting. As they did so, there was an intense flash of fire across several of the wrecked coaches at the front of the express, and fire began to spread quickly across the tangled and impacted debris. The majority of the coaches of the express were illuminated by oil-gas lighting, stored in cylinders at 85lb psi ($6kg/cm^2$) pressure, underneath the coach bodywork. As the wreckage telescoped, part of the pipework feeding gas from the many cylinders on board was fractured, and it was quickly ignited by red-hot coals spilled out from the overturned locomotives.

Many passengers were helplessly trapped in the forward part of the train, despite several gallant rescue attempts, including those of a locomotive crew which had come down the line from Hawes Junction when the flickering red glow in the early morning sky signified the extent of the accident. The crash took place in a fairly inaccessible part of the railway, and effective fire-fighting efforts were minimal. Apart from the rearmost brake van, all the express carriages were burnt out. Nine passengers lost their lives.

FIRE TRAINS

Several pre-1900 railway companies took the threat of fires on board trains and in railway premises seriously enough to warrant the provision of fire trains. These were literally rail-borne fire engines consisting of several carriages together with an ancillary covered tool van, all painted red and coupled together as one short train, and usually located at a major workshop centre.

Quite an array of hose, manual pumps, short ladders, axes and salvage equipment was carried on board, as well as a water tank of some 3,000 gallons capacity. A number of specially-trained workshop and other railway staff would be on notice quickly to man the train in the event of a fire on the company's line.

A locomotive in steam, perhaps nominally engaged on shunting duties, would also be earmarked for motive power. The whole train could be under way in about fifteen minutes of an alarm. En route to the fire it could run at up to sixty miles per hour.

Fire trains were particularly located at Crewe (London and North Western Railway), Derby (Midland Railway) and Horwich (Lancashire and Yorkshire Railway). Each of these companies became part of the London Midland and Scottish Railway in 1923, and then in turn part of the nationalised British Railways empire in 1948. All fire trains were finally decommissioned in September 1952, by which time the nationwide mobility and organisation of the fire brigade had done away with the need for such local arrangements for railway fire protection.

The memory of fire trains does, however, live on. On the preserved Bluebell Railway in West Sussex, volunteer staff man such a train that includes a 5,000 gallon oil tank now converted to carry water, allowing county firemen to connect their hoses to the precious supply. Why the need? Well, during dry spells, hundreds of acres of standing cereal crops and woodland remote from country lanes, yet adjacent to the track are at risk. From sparks from passing preserved steam locomotives, of course!

*1928 was a particularly
bad year for serious railway accidents. One such
crash, at Charfield in
Gloucestershire on the
LMS main line between
Gloucester and Bristol,
added the dimension of
fire to the death and destruction that occured at
this quiet country station.*

*In the pre-dawn
darkness of 13 October, a
non-stop Bristol-bound
passenger and mail train
express travelling at
about 60mph overran a
caution signal and col-
lided with part of a goods
train that was reversing
out of the path of the
express into a siding. The
express not only ploughed
into the trucks of the
goods train, but also hit
another goods train
travelling on an adjacent
track in the opposite
direction.*

*The first impact took
place in a deep cutting
bridged by a road. The
express carriages crashed
into the bridge abut-
ments, causing virtual
wholesale disintegration
of the wooden vehicles.*

The Hawes Junction accident was the first to involve a fire fed by a carriage gas-lighting system which was in widespread use across the country and which, combined with the timber construction of most rolling-stock of this time, posed a grave and obvious danger to passengers in the event of fire. It was some twenty years before carriage lighting by gas was fully replaced by electricity and even then, for a further two decades and more, gas cylinders on restaurant and buffet coaches remained a fire hazard.

Quintinshill (22 May 1915)

This railway accident was the worst ever to have taken place in the United Kingdom and was another case where fire added to the huge loss of life caused by high-speed collision. Quintinshill was the location of a remote signal box on the Caledonian main line just over the Scottish border, and was about 10 miles (16km) north of Carlisle. The signalman at Quintinshill controlled not only the normal passage of main-line traffic, but also was able to divert slower trains into 'waiting' loops off both up and down main lines.

On this fateful morning, the off-going signalman was late in being relieved by his day-shift colleague. By the time that the latecomer arrived at about 06.30 hours, his colleague had stationary goods trains stopped in both up and down loops, and had allowed a northbound local passenger train to cross from its normal 'down' line to the 'up' main line. It had stopped only 65yd (59m) from the signal box on the 'wrong line'. This latter move was necessary to allow a late-running down Scottish express to pass.

Soon after the changeover of signalmen took place, the fireman of the local passenger train arrived in the signal box in accordance with a rule that required a train crew to ensure that a signalman was aware of the train's presence, in this case on the 'wrong line'. The fireman signed the train register but left without checking that locking devices had been placed on the up-line signal levers. Had he done so, he would have realised that his train and its passengers were completely vulnerable to traffic from the north. About two minutes later, the relieving signalman accepted a southbound troop train conveying the 7th Battalion Royal Scots, and not long after he pulled off the signals for the late-running northbound Scottish express. The scene was now set for an absolute disaster of huge proportion.

Some minutes later, the southbound troop train, running under clear signals, came into view, moving very fast down the falling gradient from the north. The engine crew of the troop train had no chance of stopping before they ploughed into the locomotive and carriages of the local passenger train standing right in the speeding troop train's path. The enormous impact drove the carriages of the local back 136yd (124m) down the line. The engine of the waiting train was pushed back 40yd (36m), whilst the engine and tender of the troop train ended up on its side, spread virtually across all four tracks. Most of the fifteen wooden coaches full of soldiers were smashed to pieces with severe telescoping. The carriages were all gas lit; the cylinders had been topped right up before departure.

As the stunned signalmen recoiled in horror at the carnage before them, the northbound 600ton (tonne) Scottish express, running fast under signals at the clear position, hove into sight. Despite an emergency brake application, the train was still travelling at some 60 miles (96km) per hour when it careered into the widespread wreckage of the earlier collision. Locomotives, coaches and goods trucks now piled up all across the tracks in haphazard heaps of tangled wreckage, while fire was breaking out deep beneath the metal and timber debris and spreading fast. It was an awful scene, with very many passengers still trapped in the crumpled wreckage of the five trains involved.

Some primitive hand extinguishers were used in early attempts to quell the flames, but as the fire was fed from the many high-pressure gas cylinders in the wreckage, they were useless. A manual pump was quickly brought to the scene and supplied from a nearby stream. Water was also drawn from the tanks of the undamaged engines of the two goods trains. The Carlisle Fire Brigade arrived at about 10.00 hours but their efforts were of little use, as the huge and intense fire burned on, slowly engulfing the spreadeagled pile of wreckage. When, twenty-three hours later, firemen of the Carlisle Brigade left the scene, 15 coaches of the troop train, 4 carriages of the express and 5 goods wagons had all been totally destroyed by fire. Even the coal from the engine tenders added to the conflagration during the time that gas fed the inferno.

Because the nominal roll of the troop train was lost in the fire, the precise number of soldiers on board was not known. However, it is estimated that 215 officers and men were killed, as well as 10 civilian passengers in the express and local trains. In addition, 245 persons were seriously injured.

At the subsequent inquiry, the accident inspector emphasised that once again the terrible danger of fire caused by escaping gas had been a factor in the number of lives lost, and he urged its abolition. He also recommended the replacement of wooden rolling-stock with more all-steel vehicles, and stressed the need for more fire extinguishers to be carried on all passenger trains.

Sadly, further railway collisions where fire quickly broke out took place — notably at Charfield in Gloucestershire on 13 October 1928 — before such incidents thankfully became a thing of the past. But fire on board

(continued)
As compressed gas stored in cylinders under the carriages ignited, fire took quick hold and cremated many unfortunate passengers who were trapped in the compacted and twisted wreckage.

The inferno burned for twelve hours, despite the efforts of both local firemen and crews from Gloucester and Bristol. Fifteen passengers lost their lives including two young children whose identity was never discovered. Just how two such youngsters came to be on an early morning express train remains a mystery as did the precise cause of the accident. The two young unidentified travellers were buried in an unnamed grave in Charfield churchyard — a solitary reminder of one of history's transport fire tragedies.

a train in motion was still a real threat even some years later.

Taunton Sleeping-car Train Fire

In the early hours of 6 July 1978, the 21.30 Penzance to Paddington sleeper was crossing the Devon/Somerset border when a small fire started in the vestibule of one of the sleeping cars. The design of the carriages allowed forced-air ventilation to be conveyed to the individual sleeping compartments by ducting, and as the train headed steadily towards London, smoke was fed into each compartment by the ventilation system.

The awful situation that befell the sleeping occupants was compounded by the fact that it was the practice for the stewards to lock the external doors of the sleeping cars to prevent unauthorised entry at the train's various stopping points. Those travellers who became aware of the thickening smoke could not easily get away from the spreading fire and fumes, which were greatly exacerbated by the plastic decor materials and the flammable furnishings on board. Once the fire was discovered, the train came to a rapid halt on the Exeter side of Taunton station, and units of Somerset Fire Brigade were quickly on the scene, although firemen in breathing apparatus had to force entry into the various carriages now involved in the fire.

Sadly, twelve passengers died in this incident, which was thought to have started when bags of soiled linen were piled up against a heater. Since this tragedy, and having regard for the lessons of Taunton, British Rail sleeping cars have been completely redesigned. The most important of these improvements is the fitting of self-closing internal doors, alarm sounders in each compartment and an automatic smoke detector fire-alarm system covering each sleeping car. Had sleeping cars possessed these features at the time of the Taunton tragedy, the loss of life might well have been less serious.

SHIPPING

Fires afloat have always posed many problems and dangers to firemen, not least that of simply getting aboard and staying there with sufficient fire-fighting equipment. To extinguish the fire on a burning ship can be difficult, as the flames can spread easily by readily conducted heat passed on through the metal bulkheads. Means of access for firemen down into the various sections of a vessel are few, cramped and restricted. In addition, the stability of a vessel has to be critically monitored. Some of these difficulties are highlighted in the following accounts of fire aboard ship.

Pacific Glory Tanker Fire

One of the worst British offshore ship fires occurred on

(Inset) *An early example of a self-propelled steam London fireboat, the* Beta *of 1898. Designed specially for Thames fire-fighting, the* Beta *had a draught of only nineteen inches to enable her to get in very close to riverside buildings at low tide. Note large water monitor forward of wheelhouse, and Tower Bridge and period shipping in middle distance* (London Fire Brigade)

The fully laden 77,000 ton oil tanker Pacific Glory *burns furiously off the Isle of Wight after a collision and explosion in which thirteen of her crew were killed. Here Southampton Fire Brigade's fireboat puts up a cooling water curtain as firemen prepare to go aboard. The battle to put out the fire and make the vessel safe lasted for forty-four hours. 24 October 1970* (Hampshire Fire Brigade)

23 October 1970 aboard the *Pacific Glory*, a fully laden 77,000 ton (78,230 tonne) oil tanker some 6 miles (10km) out in the English Channel, off the Isle of Wight. The *Pacific Glory* had been in collision with a smaller vessel when, soon after, a series of huge explosions shook the entire ship. Thirteen of her crew were killed outright, and the aft section of the tanker was totally enveloped in fire. The survivors abandoned ship, leaving her burning in a very busy shipping area.

The first report of the fire arrived at Hampshire Fire Brigade control at 22.38 hours and firemen from both Hampshire and Portsmouth brigades prepared to embark on tugs, taking with them fire-fighting equipment. Also mobilised to the scene was the Southampton Fire Brigade fireboat. Very soon after the first report of the fire, 'Operation Solfire' was activated. This was a plan involving the combined resources of fire, police, ambulance, hospital, Royal Navy and RAF.

By early morning, the first cooling jets were being used to good effect by firemen working off the tugs. At 03.20 hours, the first fire crews boarded the stricken and abandoned tanker and before long the oil fire inside the

FIREBOATS

Floating fire engines or fireboats properly emerged as part of the Victorian steam age. Before this period, occasional efforts had been made during large riverside fires in London and other cities to put manually-pumped fire engines onto suitable river craft from which could be directed a water jet onto the riverside face of a building on fire. These had a limited effect.

However, the coming of steam-powered fire engines soon saw specially commissioned 'fire floats' in use at dockside and shipborne fires. These first fireboats were in fact vessels without engines, but in whose hull was installed a steam firepump and boiler. It was propelled to fires by a steam tug, whose crew would lash the float alongside during fire-fighting operations.

In the capital, firemen from the Metropolitan Fire Brigade tended the float's boiler and provided and manned immensely powerful water jets from the vessel's fire pump, lifting endless supplies of water from the Thames.

With the growing fire risk in London's dockland, the River Branch of the London Fire Brigade was well established by the turn of the century, and by 1912 three permanent fireboat stations were in use along the Thames. Each had by this date a self-propelled fireboat of shallow draft, able to operate on the shallowest of tides.

The further development of vessels saw the progressive introduction of diesel-engined fireboats on the Thames, including the *Massey Shaw* of 1935 which took a very active part in the Dunkirk evacuations of May 1940.

During the war, and with the subsequent nationalisation of the Fire Service, many standard pattern NFS fireboats were introduced in coastal and large river waterways to supplement the various port fireboats provided in pre-war years.

Today, the London Fire Brigade's only active fireboat, the *London Phoenix*, a catamaran built in 1985, probably represents the ultimate in modern fireboat design. Although a number of those fire brigades with maritime risks have arrangements rapidly to utilise suitable large craft in the event of a ship fire, both Devon Fire and Rescue Service and Cleveland County Fire Brigade still operate traditional fireboats on and around the waterways of Plymouth Sound and the Tees respectively. However, several other brigades provide 'inshore fireboats' of an inflatable type.

ship's tanks appeared to be coming under some control. Unfortunately, the weather was fast deteriorating and the fireboat and other supporting vessels were unable at first to get alongside the *Pacific Glory* with desperately needed foam stocks. However, by midday enough supplies and firemen were on board to continue an effective attack on the superstructure fire, although there was a threat of further explosion.

Then, quite suddenly, the fire worsened and threatened to engulf much of the tanker once again. Although firemen resolutely fought an intense battle to knock down the wall of fire, they were continually forced to retreat and eventually to abandon the vessel, finally leaving her at about 18.00 hours. However, crews stood by to re-board as the tugs struggled to pull the helpless and blazing ship out towards deeper water, while weather conditions continued to worsen.

A fresh fire-fighting assault was made at 01.00 the next morning, and firemen from four brigades pressed home their determined attack, both on board and from close by, under extremely difficult and dangerous conditions. The fires were eventually under full control by late afternoon, some forty-four hours after the first alarm. The vessel was declared safe from further fire and explosion by early evening, although some pollution through oil leakage was still taking place. It was, indeed, the successful end to a very hazardous and arduous operation.

The MV *Ebn Magid* – Portland, Dorset

This fire, which started on 28 January 1986, was a graphic illustration of just how difficult ship fires can be. The 7,400 ton (7,500 tonne) MV *Ebn Magid* was twenty-one miles south of Portland Bill when traces of smoke were first seen issuing from No 2 hold. She was laden with a general cargo, including cattle feed, pharmaceutical supplies and cocoa powder, and was en route to Tripoli out of Antwerp.

On discovering the fire the ship's master, a West German, operated the carbon-dioxide fire suppression system in an attempt to extinguish the fire. This attempt was unsuccessful, and soon afterwards a call for assistance was made to HM Coastguard, Portland. HMS *Manchester* and the German warship *Neidersachsen*, which were in the area at the time, responded and began to escort the *Ebn Magid* towards Poole. At the same time the divisional commander of Dorset Fire Brigade 'A' Division proceeded to the HM Coastguard's control centre at Portland to commence the collation of all necessary information and co-ordination of the brigade's actions.

On arrival at Portland, the divisional commander learnt that the burning vessel was now heading for the Portland Royal Naval base. The fire appeared to be contained in No 2 hold, and fortunately no crew members were missing or injured. Sea conditions were moderate to rough and the wind was about Force 5 to 7. It was understood that a dangerous cargo was also on board but attempts by radio failed to obtain any information regarding its location and type. The possibility of winching a fire-brigade officer onto the ship by helicopter was discussed, but the RNAS Lee-on-Solent considered this too dangerous, bearing in mind the sea conditions. It was then decided that the ship would not be permitted to enter Portland Harbour, but would be anchored in Weymouth Bay, to be met by a fire-brigade reconnaissance party led by the divisional commander and two other officers. A message to the ship's master requested that he should make available the ship and cargo plans and manifest.

On the information received at this stage it appeared that the fire was still confined to No 2 hold. However, at the time of the discovery of the fire, the ship's master had unfortunately discharged his entire stock of carbon dioxide, which seemed to have little effect. When the fire-service reconnaissance party boarded the *Ebn Magid* at

21.25 hours, the fire situation had deteriorated. This first reconnaissance revealed smoke and heat in both No 2 and No 3 holds. The ship's crew were cooling the hatch covers of No 2 hold with jets from the ship's main. Access from the accommodation decks to the forward hold was extremely difficult, due to deck cargo consisting of containers and cars, a factor which was to have a major bearing on subsequent events.

At this time the seat of the fire was still regarded as being in the aft section of No 2 hold on the starboard side, although it was difficult to assess at which level this was, and it was considered that the fire in No 3 hold was caused by heat being conducted through the bulkhead. The ship's manifest showed a large quantity of highly flammable ethanol and butanol in No 1 hold, with No 2 and No 3 holds containing cattle feed, rubber, pharmaceutical supplies and other general cargo. A second reconnaissance confirmed a worsening of the situation, and the divisional commander made the decision that, due to the sea state and logistical requirements, it was not feasible to fight this fire at sea. In answer to a request for assistance made to the queen's harbour master, the Royal Navy decided to allow the ship to be berthed alongside in Portland Harbour to allow fire fighting to commence. Arrangements could then be made for the ship to be met by all necessary firemen and equipment, and in addition there would be port facilities for the removal of the deck and hatch covers.

At the same time it was decided that the fire-fighting recommendations to the chief fire officer, who was awaiting the ship's arrival, would be (a) to protect the bulkhead with cooling jets between Nos 1 and 2 holds, with the removal of containers and cars from hatch covers of Nos 1 and 3 holds; (b) to remove hazardous cargo within No 2 hold adjacent to the bulkhead, and to make a fire-fighting attack on No 2 hold. Just before the ship was docked at Portland at 00.19 hours on 29 January, it was clear that the six hours which had elapsed since the discovery of the first smoke had allowed the fire in the hold to develop virtually unchecked. As the *Ebn Magid* tied up to the quay, the chief fire officer took command.

There now began a major fire-fighting operation to save the vessel and its cargo. It was beset by many difficulties, the first of these being that the removal of the considerable deck cargo, including containers and cars, was clearly going to be a protracted job. The first breathing-apparatus crews who attempted to penetrate down into the heat and thick smoke of No 2 hold found cargo stowed to within a few inches of the access ladders. No 3 hold was found to be similarly full of cargo, and here the fire was also beginning to take a serious hold.

By dawn on the Wednesday morning, the covers of No 1 hold were fully open and although the bulkheads

(Overleaf) The difficulties of fire-fighting at sea are well illustrated in this view of the 7,500 tons Ebn Magid as a serious fire burns deep in the hold of the freighter off Portland, Dorset. Fortunately, the sea is fairly calm at this stage but note the number of tugs and tenders necessary to support a major breathing apparatus attack on the fire. Eight thousand man hours were expended before the fire was under control, and fire-fighting was complicated by uncertainties over the vessel's cargo. Firemen also had to contend with extremely difficult access into the hot and smoky holds, as can be seen from the cars stored on top of containers which in turn are obstructing cargo hatches. 28 January 1986 (Press Assocation)

THE FIERY THAMES

A convoy of six fireboats which had been ordered back to London from the Thameshaven fires, came up to Woolwich Reach just before midnight. The officer commanding this small flotilla described the scene:

'We kept close formation until we reached Woolwich, and then we saw an extraordinary spectacle. There was nothing but fire ahead, apparently stretching right across the river and burning on both its banks. We seemed to be entering a tunnel of fire – no break in it anywhere. All the usual landmarks were obliterated by walls of flame. Burning barges drifted past. For many hours no contact with the shore was possible. We did what we could where we could as we slowly worked our way up-river.

At one time we were just getting into position to fight a fire in a large warehouse when the whole of the riverside front collapsed into the water with a mighty splash. The contents of the building, bags of beans, pouring into the river made a sound like a tropical rain storm.'

were hot and smoke present, there was no fire. The drums of highly flammable ethanol and butanol were removed under the cover of cooling water sprays. Soon after, full fire-fighting access into No 2 hold was possible, but No 3 hold was now found to contain many cars not shown on the ship's stowage plan. These vehicles had been placed right on top of other cargo, which included drums of oil. The seat of the fire, thought to be in the bagged animal feed, lay beneath.

The fire situation continued to worsen and all firemen were withdrawn from the ship to positions on the dockside. Another unsuccessful attempt was made to inject carbon dioxide brought in bulk from Bristol, and yet another problem arose, one ever present in ship fire-fighting – the stability of the vessel. The *Ebn Magid* had taken on a list to starboard of about 8 degrees, but this was soon corrected by pumping ballast water to port to compensate for the fire-fighting water being used.

Because of the worsening situation, a decision – made after consultations with the parties concerned – was taken to beach the ship in Portland Harbour. This was achieved at 08.40 hours on Thursday morning. The *Ebn Magid* was now lying in 26ft (8m) of water, approximately 800yd (732m) from the shoreline. The fire was now also burning freely in No 3 hold and the RNAS salvage vessel *Kinbrace* was moored on the starboard side to become a fire-fighting platform in addition to the forward control point. Apart from fire-fighting measures taken to quell the fires in Nos 2 and 3 holds, it was feared that the engine-room and accommodation decks would become involved. To avoid this, cooling jets were brought to bear in the engine-room to protect the bulkhead, and this, after some considerable time, had the effect of controlling the rising heat levels.

During the early evening all the ship's lighting failed, along with the ship's water main, and the temperature levels on the engine-room bulkhead began to increase significantly. Bearing this in mind, with men working in darkness below decks and with the possibility of bulkhead failure, on the advice of a Royal Navy salvage expert all firemen were withdrawn and accounted for. Fire-fighting operations continued from the *Kinbrace* with additional jets to protect the exposed section of engine-room bulkhead. Thermal imaging cameras were used extensively throughout this stage.

As the chief fire officer was now certain that the lower hold was completely involved in fire, it was decided to flood that section of the *Ebn Magid*, and by 1 February the fires had been largely extinguished, apart from a number of deck containers which had caught fire through conducted heat from below.

When, on 4 February, the fires were finally declared out and the ship safe, over 8,000 fire-fighting man hours had been expended on the operation. A total of 34 pumps attended the fire, along with 7 special appliances, drawing on the resources of every fire station in Dorset Fire Brigade; 20 main jets and 4 fixed monitor jets were used and, at one stage, 120 breathing-apparatus sets were in use. The recharging and servicing of these sets over the days of the *Ibn Magid* fire were in themselves major logistical tasks.

The *Ibn Magid* was eventually refloated and a considerable amount of its cargo found to be salvageable. The cause of the fire was thought to have been the spontaneous ignition, on drying out, of animal feed loaded in a damp state at Antwerp.

AIRCRAFT

One of the very worst types of transportation fire is that involving an aircraft full of passengers. Such a horrendous fire, at Manchester International Airport, hit the headlines in 1985, and drew worldwide attention to the problems of the rapid evacuation of passenger aircraft.

The Manchester Air Disaster

Whilst commencing its take-off run at approximately 07.13 hours on 22 August 1985 a charter aircraft – Boeing 737, Flight KT328 – of British Airtours, carrying 131 passengers and 6 crew, suddenly became involved in a serious fire. The fire, on the port side of the aircraft, actuated a fire alarm on the flight deck and at the same time was observed by personnel manning air traffic control. The 'Crash Alarm' at the airport fire station was sounded, whence four appliances responded. The aircraft was visible from the fire station and was still on the main runway when the appliances turned out from the station. The Aircraft Fire Service proceeded towards the aircraft, which then turned off the main runway and came to rest.

There was a severe fire in progress which was rapidly developing and involving the port wing and rear passenger compartment. Burning fuel was being discharged from tanks in the port wing, and large volumes of smoke were enveloping the aircraft, obliterating visibility from the mid-fuselage area to the rear of the plane. Fire-fighting operations using foam commenced approximately thirty seconds after the plane came to a stop. During this initial attack on the fire, both forward escape chutes were deployed, enabling some passengers to escape. Other passengers were able to escape over the starboard wing of the aircraft. Two foam-making appliances were then re-positioned and further foam was applied to the developing fire situation.

At 07.15 hours, Greater Manchester Fire Service received a request from the Airport Fire Service, in accordance with predetermined support arrangements. Seven appliances were despatched immediately to the

airport, the first arriving only five minutes later.

On arrival at the scene, the officer in charge of the Greater Manchester Fire Service appliances could see that the aircraft was involved in a severe fire and arranged for the 400gal (1,800 litres) of water from each of his pumps to be transferred to the tanks of the airport foam appliances, before hydrant supplies were brought into use. Two airport firemen donned breathing apparatus and attempted to make entry by way of the starboard wing escape door. Four more breathing-apparatus wearers of Greater Manchester Fire Service made entry into the aircraft, using the starboard and front starboard doors. Fire-fighting inside was carried out using foam branches from the airport foam appliance.

At 07.30 hours, Station Officer McIntosh sent the following radio message to Greater Manchester Fire Control: 'Boeing 737. Whole aircraft on fire. Persons trapped. Foam being applied by Airport Fire Service. Breathing apparatus, jets, fire-fighting and rescue in progress.'

A message requesting a further six pumping appliances was sent at 07.32 hours. At this stage, it was not known exactly how many persons were on the aircraft, but as firemen gained entrance into the main fuselage area it was immediately obvious that this fire had caused a very high loss of life. The fire had already involved the passenger compartment and it was immediately attacked, using both foam jets and water jets supplied through the airport appliances, although access to the aircraft was difficult, being over the starboard wing and via the front starboard escape door. During this stage of the operation, one man was found still breathing but trapped under several bodies. He was recovered from the aircraft and handed to ambulance personnel, who removed him to hospital.

Because of the large amount of fuel that had been discharged onto the runway and the position of the aircraft and fire-fighting crews, possible re-ignition of this spilt fuel was a hazard. Further application of foam throughout the fire-fighting operations were therefore made. The extinction of pockets of fire inside the fuselage of the Boeing, and the search for and recovery of bodies, continued throughout the morning before confirmation was given at 14.04 hours that all persons on board had been accounted for.

Fifty-five of the 137 passengers and crew on board perished in this awful fire. The incident served to highlight the ever-present problem of speedy escape from fire on board an aircraft, and certainly focused international attention on the need for better emergency lighting, and more widespread use of non-flammable compartment furnishings.

Another view of the devastated Boeing 737 on the taxiway at Manchester International Airport. The intensity of the fire has caused the Boeing's tail section to collapse. The foam used by fire-fighters in their initial attack is still visible around and under the aircraft. Note the terminal buildings and other aircraft in the far distance. 22 August 1985 (Greater Manchester Fire Service)

TRAGEDIES

Fire tragedies of past years have not merely brought about a safer environment for the public at large. In a number of cases, the deaths of firemen have led directly to improvement in fire-fighting equipment, procedures and training.

One such tragic incident occured at the Smithfield Meat Market, London, in the early hours of 23 January 1958. Smoke had been discovered in the vast labyrinth of basements beneath the market hall, and deteriorating conditions soon saw many breathing apparatus crews being committed into the thickening smoke of the basement to search for and to locate the seat of the fire.

The basements were thermally insulated and included many refrigerated stores, constituting a veritable maze of walkways, corridors and tunnels. During the early stages of search for the fire, two breathing apparatus-clad fire-fighters, a Station Officer and a fireman, failed to emerge from the basement when expected, and fresh rescue teams were sent into the now dense smoke to locate the missing team.

After an hour of the most diligent and careful searching in the thick and swirling black smoke now obviously coming from the burning cork insulation of the basement, the two missing firemen were found unconscious and partially buried under hundreds of collapsed frozen meat parcels. They were rushed out to fresh air and to nearby St Bartholomew's Hospital, but to no avail. Both were dead on arrival, having suffocated in the smoke when their oxygen supply of about fifty minutes ran out. The fire continued to burn unseen through ducting and ventilation shafts for many hours before firemen were able to encourage it to vent to open air, and discharge its pent-up energy as angry orange flame. It was 40 hours before the fire was under control, with 389 pumps and over 1,700 officers and men involved, many still using breathing apparatus in that awful basement. The Central Market Hall was badly damaged but the fire was prevented from spreading beyond the market curtilage.

The outcome of this tragedy was that a new breathing apparatus procedure was adopted nationally to prevent the recurrence of such an incident. This required adaptations to the breathing sets themselves in order to provide an audible warning to wearers that their oxygen supply was running out. Those two firemen did not give their lives in vain as, although firemen have since been killed whilst wearing breathing apparatus, it has never been in such tragic circumstances as those which took place at Smithfield over thirty years ago.

Another such tragedy that led directly to safer procedures being adopted nationwide took place at Dudgeon's Wharf, Millwall, East London, on 17 July 1969. The premises concerned were a large collection of cylindrical oil and fuel tanks directly alongside the River Thames. Several empty tanks were in various stages of being cut up and dismantled. Only two weeks earlier, eight pumps and forty firemen had dealt with a large outbreak of fire on the site, involving empty tanks. There followed some liaison between the contractors and officers of the London Fire Brigade as to safe cutting methods that could be applied to the dismantling of the empty tanks.

But on 17 July tragedy struck. In response to another call to the site to a fire in Tank 97 which was in the early stages of dismantlement, three pumps with their crews quickly arrived at the scene. Tank 97 was 35 feet high and had a potential capacity of 125,000 gallons. The fire in the tank appeared to have died down, and during the course of opening up an access cover into the base of the tank, an explosion occurred, blowing off the massive circular steel roof of the tank upon which five firemen were standing. All five were killed instantly, together with a civilian worker.

The subsequent Inquiry found that there was a need for a greater awareness of such explosive dangers, and that the communication of information relating to such sites as Dudgeon's Wharf could be improved. There were also various recommendations involving the Factory Inspectorate.

That sad day at Dudgeon's Wharf has never been forgotten by the British Fire Service, nor has the earlier sacrifice of Smithfield. A fire-fighter attempts to carry out what at times is a very dangerous job in a safe manner, having high regard for those men who have been killed in action at incidents where there have been manifest lessons to be learnt.

8 AFTER THE DEED

It is a sad fact that for over a century, compulsory public fire-safety measures have only been introduced after a fire disaster where there has been a major loss of life.

'Stable-door' legislation has been the direct result of such fire tragedies, which in each successive case has over the years given a progressively increased burden to firemen as their role has widened to become active preventers of fire, fire deaths and injury.

The major instances of fire which gave rise to new fire safety legislation include the following examples.

Theatre Royal, Exeter, Devon (5 September 1887) 188 lives lost

During a performance in front of a packed house, fire broke out backstage and spread into the auditorium with great rapidity. In the subsequent chaos and stampede for the few exits, compounded by the spreading fire and smoke, 188 people lost their lives. After the fire was out, the majority of the bodies were found piled up against each other inside the exit doors. It is still today the world's worst theatre fire tragedy.

Outcome: Major inquiry was ordered by the home secretary and undertaken by Captain Eyre Massey Shaw, London's Chief Fire Officer. Shaw's recommendations for properly marked and illuminated fire exits of sufficient width and number, partitioning of the auditorium by means of a safety curtain, and regular inspections of these safety features, became embodied in the Theatres Act, 1888.

M. & M. Mart Garage, Ashley Road, Bristol (24 November 1951) 11 dead

This major incident occurred whilst a petrol tanker was discharging its load into the underground fuel tanks of the garage. There was a sudden rush of flame from the tank-filling point, followed immediately by a huge explosion and fire. As this was mid-morning in a city-centre location, many passers-by were engulfed, as well as those working in and around the garage. The explosion demolished buildings all around, and free-flowing fuel spread the fire in all directions.

The ensuing inquiry heard that the likely cause of the tragedy was a spark from electrical apparatus igniting vapour from an overfilled storage tank.

HEROISM

Amongst the would-be rescuers at the scene during the early stages of the Exeter Theatre Royal fire of 3 September 1877 was one Able Seaman William Hunt, RN, at that time serving on HMS *Express*. Hunt was personally responsible for the rescue of many theatre-goers, working with several others quite relentlessly and without regard for his own safety as the intensity of the fire developed.

In his subsequent statement to the Coroner Able Seaman Hunt said that at one stage he peered through smoke into a window leading onto the gallery stairs. What he saw sickened him, and turning away he said helplessly, 'I could do no good there'. Many of the 188 people who died in this awful fire tragedy were literally piled up, one upon the other, in that corner of the building. Hunt, who had himself seen many harsh sights during his naval service, would never again speak of his Theatre Royal experience, his rescue work or of the human suffering that was all around him on that fateful evening.

A dramatic painting by Frederick
Ford of the Theatre Royal, Exeter,
fire of 5 September 1887 which
claimed 188 lives and led to an
improvement in fire exit and other
safety requirements in theatres
(Ford family collection)

Firemen seach amongst the rubble
that was a Bristol petrol station
and garage after a huge explosion
and fire have wrecked the
premises. Eleven people died in
this incident which led to more
stringent electrical equipment at
petrol stations. M and M Mart
Garage, Bristol. 24 November
1951 (Bristol Evening World)

Outcome: Amendments to the Petroleum Legislation of 1928 and 1939, leading to safer transference arrangements of bulk petrol.

Eastwood Mills, Lorne Street, Keighley, West Yorkshire (23 February 1956) 8 fatalities

The premises, which held a Fire Certificate under the Factories Act 1951, consisted of three storeys and an attic. There was an internal stairway at one end and an internal flight of stairs at the other end between the attic and third floor, with access to an external stairway.

The fire was started by a plumber's blowlamp at ground floor level and spread rapidly over the ground-floor ceiling. The plumber attempted to extinguish the fire without raising the alarm. The fire spread up the main stairway, assisted by a nearby vertical shaft. Smoke also prevented persons in the attic from reaching the external stairway.

A cashier called the fire brigade on the instructions of the work's engineer, but rescue was hampered by the impending collapse of the building. The following day, seven bodies (six women and one man) were found near the head of the main stairs. Another body, that of a boy of sixteen, was found in a nearby lavatory.

The burning remains of Eastwood Mills, Keighley in which eight employees died having failed to get out when the fire was first discovered. This tragedy led to tighter requirements for means of escape in the Factories Act which for the first time placed the legal responsibility for checking fire exits on the fire service. 23 February 1956 (Keighley News)

The inquiry heard that there was no fire alarm system, and no fire exit signs at Eastwood Mills. No staff training or fire drills had been given. All these aspects of safety were required in the original Factories Act. It was thought that at the time of the fire, approximately 25,000 other 'factory' premises up and down the country were in a similar parlous state. Indeed, *Hansard* of 16 May 1956 records the home secretary's concern:

I have made enquiries and I find that the Factory Inspectors can only visit factories once in five years. I have decided, therefore, to place responsibility for means of escape in case of fire under the Factories Act of 1936 on Fire Authorities, who through the members of their Brigade and their extensive knowledge of how buildings and their contents behave when on fire make them admirably suited for this responsibility.

Outcome: The Factories Act was amended to transfer the responsibility for means of escape in case of fire to fire authorities. As a postscript, the occupiers of the mill were charged under Section 36(7) of the Factories Act 1937, found guilty and fined £15.

Henderson's Departmental Store, Church Street, Liverpool (22 June 1960)
11 dead

Henderson's consisted of a five-storey building with basement and sub-basement, having several stairways, only one of which was enclosed. A fire alarm system was installed, but at the time of the fire was not connected to the power supply. The fire was caused by a fault in the electric cabling, between the third and fourth floors.

Persons were prevented from escaping because doors to the enclosed staircase were open, and smoke rapidly filled the store areas. On arrival, the fire brigade

Neighbours look on at the burnt-out shell of the Top Storey Club in Bolton, Lancashire, the morning after a fire rapidly swept through the building. Nineteen persons perished when they were unable to make their escape or jumped to their deaths. This fire led to a strengthening of the licensing regulations and fire exits from such drinking clubs. 1 May 1961 (Associated Press)

found normal business being carried out on lower floors because people were quite unaware of the serious fire on the upper storeys. Ten people were rescued through windows by firemen, but 10 shoppers died in the fire, together with 1 person who fell off a ledge.

Outcome: The Offices, Shops and Railway Premises Act, 1963. This specified, amongst other requirements, the need for an effective fire alarm system, and the regular testing of such.

Top Storey Club, Crown Street, Bolton, Lancs (1 May 1961) 19 fatalities

The club was housed in an old converted premises on the third floor, served only by a single staircase and unprotected by fire doors. During the late evening, a fire started in an unoccupied joinery workshop on the ground floor of the building. It spread very quickly to the single timber staircase, trapping all those upstairs in the club. A number of people smashed windows and jumped to their deaths, while others perished in the thickening smoke on the third floor before firemen could beat back the fire and get to the helpless victims. The cause of the fire was never determined.

Outcome: The Licensing Act 1961 which enabled fire-prevention officers to require proper means of escape and other fire-safety measures in such clubs as the Top Storey.

Rose and Crown Hotel, Market Place, Saffron Walden, Essex (26 December 1969) 11 dead

This fire, which broke out at 01.47 hours, started in a downstairs lounge and very quickly filled the entire upper floors and corridors with thick smoke, due to many doors having been left open. An alternative means of escape was in fact available to those residents who were trapped by the smoke, but they were unaware of its existence due to lack of 'Fire Exit' signs.

A number of people jumped from the upper floors of the hotel, and those who survived the fall suffered serious injuries. Firemen managed, however, to rescue twelve residents down ladders. The cause of the fire was believed to be a television set which had been left switched on in the ground-floor lounge.

Outcome: There were a number of similar hotel fire tragedies in London at this time, although none with a death toll as great as that at Saffron Walden. The Fire Precautions Act became effective in 1971, requiring the fire-safety certification of hotels and boarding houses.

A Christmas tragedy. Firemen clear up after the battle to save the Rose and Crown Hotel in Saffron Walden, Essex. The fire started in the early hours and was believed to have been caused when a television set was left switched on in a ground floor lounge. Eleven residents died. This and other fatal hotel fires of this period gave impetus to the Fire Precautions Act of 1971 which required more regulated fire safety measures in hotels and boarding houses. 26 December 1969 (Keystone Press Agency)

(Below) *The beginning of a disaster that shocked the world. A smouldering fire quickly grows in accumulated rubbish under the main stand of Bradford City Football Club. It was believed to have been started by a dropped cigarette end. Valley Parade, Bradford. 16 May 1985* (D. P. Hattersley)

Only sixty seconds later, the fire is now rapidly consuming the timber flooring and seating of the stand. Police officers are trying to clear the area (Bradford Telegraph and Argus)

About four minutes after the fire was first discovered at the far right end of the stand, the entire wooden structure is totally engulfed in an intense fire. Many spectators who fled to the rear exits of the stand have already perished. The policeman is using his helmet as a shield against the immense radiated heat. Fifty-six men, women and children perished in this awful tragedy (Bradford Telegraph and Argus)

Bradford City Football Club Stadium, Valley Parade, Bradford, W Yorks (11 May 1985)
56 fatalities

This fire started under a wooden spectator stand during a football match attended by a capacity crowd. The fire developed extremely rapidly, engulfing the entire stand within minutes. Many victims were found piled up against the locked exit barriers behind the stand. Many survivors suffered serious burns.

Outcome: The subsequent inquiry chaired by Mr Justice Popplewell QC, led to the Fire Safety and Safety of Places of Sport Act 1987, and an amendment to the Safety of Sports Grounds Act 1975. This legislation requires more stringent fire-safety measures at both indoor and outdoor sporting and recreational venues.

Fire Deaths – New Year 1988

Fire fatalities can occur throughout the year at any time of day or night, on weekdays, weekends or even over a holiday period. Thus on New Year's Day 1988, despite heroic rescue attempts by firemen, a father and four of his children perished in an intense fire in a semi-detached dwelling at Merthyr Tydfil in Mid Glamorgan, south Wales. The fire, like so many others in recent

The pain and suffering of fire. Spectators pour over lower barriers of the stand as fire takes hold behind them. Note the two spectators clambering over the obstacle – their clothes are actually smouldering. This fire disaster led to an Inquiry chaired by Mr Justice Popplewell Q.C. which recommended wide-ranging safety improvements to sports grounds embodied in a new Fire Safety Act of 1987. Valley Parade, Bradford. 11 May 1985 (Press Association)

The Manchester Woolworth's fire of 8 May 1979 that caused the deaths of ten shop workers and customers unable to escape the dense black smoke of burning polyurethane furniture. A team of two firemen work a cooling jet at third-floor level to ease conditions inside the store where many of their colleagues in breathing apparatus are searching for survivors. Few were found. This tragedy began the momentum towards safer furniture foam filling but it took almost another decade and many more fire fatalities before suitable legislation was effected (Manchester Evening News)

years, had been fuelled by furniture containing polyurethane foam which, when involved in fire, produces thick toxic black smoke in sufficient suffocating quantity to fill a typical house in a couple of minutes.

The Woolworth's fire in Piccadilly, Manchester, in May 1979 resulted in the loss of ten lives and was the start of a campaign, led by the fire service, to outlaw foam filling in furniture and to see it replaced with safer materials. Sadly, in the intervening years many lives were lost, being attributable to smoke from such furniture, but the Merthyr Tydfil New Year tragedy gave fresh impetus to those who demanded that enough was enough. It was the country's chief fire officers who finally succeeded in convincing the government that the time had come for new legislation towards safer furniture.

Outcome: The Furniture and Furnishings (Fire) (Safety) Regulations 1988, Statutory Instrument 1988 No 1324 which sets new fire-resistance standards for domestic upholstered furniture. These regulations come into full effect, as regards new furniture, from 1 March 1990.

Whilst this depressing catalogue of fire deaths and destruction had undoubtedly led to a safer environment for the community at large, both at work and at play, history will surely record yet more fire disasters to come. In our imperfect world, the legislators will once again strive to ensure that unnecessary fire deaths and injuries are minimised as far as is humanly possible. But that, of course, is the root of the problem. Fires don't just happen; they are caused. Indeed, the fire service has long accepted that there are three main causes of fire – namely, men, women and children!

128

9 '999' SPECIAL SERVICES

A common feature of the modern-day work of the fire service is that fire-fighters of all brigades regularly attend many '999' emergency calls to incidents other than fires. Fire brigades identify the non-fire calls as 'special services'. This type of emergency has grown to such an extent that, during 1987, the fire service in England and Wales collectively responded to almost 175,800 such individual incidents, and 5,305 persons were rescued by firemen from non-fire situations. Thus special services today represent something over 24 per cent of all '999' emergencies dealt with by all fire brigades in England and Wales.

To further emphasise the growth of special service work, it is very interesting to note that in 1927 the London Fire Brigade (then covering the old London County Council area), although the largest and operationally busiest fire brigade in the land, answered only 61 such emergency calls in the whole year. Many of these were to horses, still the prime mover on much commercial transport, becoming stuck or jammed in some predicament and at worst having fallen into basement areas after wandering off untethered. Ten years later, in 1937, London special service calls totalled a mere 123 for that year. In 1974, albeit by then comprising the enlarged area of the Greater London Council, non-fire emergencies had risen to 14,599 individual 'cries for help'. By 1987, the total number of London's special service calls had risen to a staggering 64,735 individual incidents.

One is tempted to speculate on this incredible expansion of demand for the urgent help of the fire service. Quite obviously, much of this growth is directly related to our mechanised society in all its aspects. More people than ever before have wider and more regular access to transport. Industry tries to meet the demands of the consumer boom, so that science and technology reach new heights of achievement, and hazardous substances become more evident in a greater range of manufacturing processes. And, of course, accidents still happen.

But what precisely are special service calls? In earlier years they were mostly of a humanitarian nature yet very diverse in their range. Today they are frequently road traffic accidents where a driver and passengers are perhaps trapped by the crushed impacted body of the

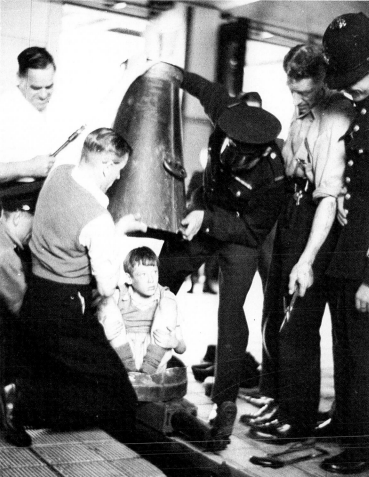

Modern jet aircraft crashes invariably involve fire but with earlier piston engine aircraft crashes, fire would not always break out. In this remarkable view, a Douglas DC3 Dakota of Railway Air Services bound for Glasgow has failed to gain height during a snowstorm after take-off from Northolt Aerodrome and ploughed into this row of terraced houses in Victoria Road, Ruislip, Middlesex. No fire broke out and fortunately, there were no serious injuries either. Note Leyland pump and hose-laying lorry, together with ladders pitched up to roof. 19 December 1946 (London Fire Brigade)

Children often provide firemen with all manner of rescue problems. Here a young boy has climbed into a milk churn and found he could not get out. A milkman took the churn to nearby Lambeth Fire Station. The print captures the moment of release after some careful work with hacksaws and tinsnips. 4 July 1947 (London Fire Brigade)

131

car, or where a leaking road or rail chemical tanker contains hazardous substances which threaten the community. The special service call can also be to a lift malfunction in a high-rise building, where a number of people have been trapped between floors in the claustrophic confines of the lift car. Children are frequently in distress with fingers and heads trapped in various mechanical predicaments, and animals of all sorts become stuck up trees or down wells. The sheer variety of such calls is seemingly endless. Often, fire service crews themselves face considerable personal danger in tackling these emergency calls, work which in many instances can be as physically taxing as pure fire-fighting.

The interesting point regarding special service calls is their legal status within the overall framework of a public fire brigade. The modern United Kingdom fire brigades were set up under the Fire Services Act of 1947 which provides for a local authority (usually a county council) to be responsible for providing and organising an effective fire brigade. In this act there is a brief mention of the fire service dealing with emergencies other than fire. The first part of Section 3 says that:

> . . . the powers of a fire authority shall include power . . . to employ the fire brigade maintained by them, or use any equipment so maintained, for purposes other than fire fighting purposes for which it appears to the authority to be suitable, and, if they think fit, to make such charge as they may determine for any services rendered in the course of such employment or use.

In practice a charge will only be levied for non-humanitarian work. One ready example where a fee would be charged is gaining access into a property on behalf of an occupier who had locked himself out and where no danger of fire existed. Similarly, some water pumping-out work would also be chargeable, depending upon the particular circumstances. However, the vast majority of special service work is by its very nature an emergency, and fire crews will respond to the '999' address as rapidly as if it were a fire call.

Interestingly, in recognition of their own changing role, several United Kingdom fire brigades have changed their title. An early example of this came in the seventies when Cambridgeshire Fire Brigade became Cambridgeshire Fire and Rescue Service. More recently, Devon, Gloucestershire and Staffordshire have similarly altered their titles to incorporate the rescue element of their work, and become Fire and Rescue Services.

Records relating to special services are imprecise, but one of the first examples of such rescue work by firemen occurred on 18 March 1913 in London's Bayswater district. Sadly it had a tragic outcome. A sewerman was reported to be overcome by gas while working about

A PAINFUL ENCOUNTER

A retired Sub Officer of the London Fire Brigade recalls an incident during his service at Brixton Fire Station:

A coal lorry pulled up outside the station and a boy jumped down from the passenger side and came to the front door as though to ask for directions. However, he sought our help for the poor driver of the lorry. Both driver and lorry had seen better days, and one of the coil springs in the old driving seat had started to protrude through the leather and horsehair from which they were then constructed.

Unfortunately the sharp end of this spring had got the driver by the scrotum which was at the one time inconvenient, painful and most embarrassing.

We clustered around him, each offering our two pennorth of advice and were about to make a 'call' of it and request an emergency tender, but the man would have none of it. He had only called in to give us warning that he would want assistance when he had finished his round!

MERCURIAL

By 1970, hazardous chemical spillages on road and rail transport were a fairly regular occurrence for firemen up and down the country. However, around this time, Ron Bentley, then the station commander at Crawley Fire Station of West Sussex Fire Brigade, discovered that a chemical incident on board an aircraft at Gatwick Airport created more than a few problems:

One night I was in charge of an attendance to a freighter aircraft in which there had been a spillage of mercury which we had attempted to recover. In the confines of an aircraft hold little globules of mercury are hard to see, let alone collect, but with the usual methodical efficiency of fire crews, it looked as if the last blob had been found when I was approached by a member of the airline staff. As always, there are tight schedules to meet, even

with freighters, and it was his intention that the appropriate 'slot' for this aircraft would not be missed and as soon as my firemen had finished with it, it would be taxied out for take-off.

Now my chemistry was never all that brilliant, but I did recollect something about mercury being slowly reactive with aluminium, and this mercury had been rolling along bare aluminium struts within the aircraft. Having dreadful visions of metal fatigue being blamed by the Air Investigation Board following some future crash of this aircraft, I 'grounded' it until it had been thoroughly inspected and passed fit to fly by ground engineering staff. Thus I found myself having to make a decision which I was neither qualified to make nor had the responsibility for, but special services are funny things.

½ mile (.8km) into a sewer under reconstruction. Two firemen wearing newly commissioned oxygen breathing-apparatus sets descended into the sewer but neither reappeared. After a time, further firemen entered the sewer and found both their colleagues unconscious. They were quickly removed to fresh air but both were beyond help. It was thought that one of the two firemen had got into some breathing difficulty and the other had removed his facemask to provide fresh oxygen to the casualty. The missing workman was later located in the sewer and he, too, was dead. This incident served to tighten up the breathing-apparatus wearing procedures which were rather haphazard at that early stage.

By the beginning of the fifties, special services were still only a very small part of firemen's work, although in the larger cities the growing trends were emerging. In 1949, London, the busiest fire brigade in the country, answered 1,170 non-fire emergency calls; in 1950 this crept up to 1,279. By the end of 1951 the total had reached 1,625, and in 1952 it climbed to a new peak at 1,985 separate non-fire emergencies right across London.

On 8 October 1952 there occurred at Harrow and Wealdstone, in Middlesex, one of the worst railway accidents ever to take place in this country. At the height of the morning peak rush hour, a London-bound express overran danger signals and ploughed at high speed into the rear of a stationary suburban train as it stood in the

The impact of railway collisions creates special rescue difficulties. This photograph of a Class 31 diesel locomotive was taken after the body of the driver had been extricated from the crushed cab following some two hours of spreading, cutting and lifting with powerful hydraulic tools. The locomotive collided at low speed with the rear of a stationary freight train, and the impact of the collision has lifted the truck bogie completely off the rails. Ilford, Essex. 29 September 1970 (London Fire Brigade)

station picking up its load of London commuters. The impact of the collision was tremendous. Some of the carriages were of traditional timber-framed construction and, although fortunately there was no fire, wreckage from the two trains reared up, piled across the platform and spilled out onto the adjacent down main line which carried trains away from the capital.

Even as the shocked and dazed signalman threw all his signals to danger, a Liverpool express, unusually on this day hauled by two locomotives, bore down upon the accident scene at speed. It was quite unable to stop in time. The heavy train careered into the wreckage, its two locomotives dragging the carriages of the Liverpool express deep into the already tangled mass of the initial crash. When the first Middlesex Fire Brigade firemen arrived several minutes later, the wreckage from the multiple collision was piled so high and widespread that the station footbridge had been demolished. Even the clock high above the station buildings had stopped at the precise moment of the massive impact of the first collision.

From a fire-service aspect, the accident very rapidly escalated into a rescue operation of major proportions. As well as reinforcing Middlesex crews arriving in some force, men from the London and Hertfordshire brigades soon brought the total of firemen searching at the scene for trapped passengers to over 150. By any scale it was a disaster. Many unfortunate passengers were killed outright either in the first or secondary collision. However, in the first couple of hours firemen were able to free some live casualties from the wreckage, although as in all such major accidents the obviously dead had to wait for extrication until all the visibly live casualties had been released.

In all, firemen worked in shifts for over four days and nights until all the final victims were located and recovered. A total of 118 passengers lost their lives in this disaster and it is particularly poignant to record that one of the dead was a serving fire-brigade officer, Station Officer William Reid, who was attached to Penrith Fire Station of Cumberland Fire Brigade and was travelling south in the London-bound express en route to join a course at the Fire Service College at Dorking, Surrey. Sadly, he only reached Harrow and Wealdstone, an outer London suburban railway station whose name, on that fateful October morning, was indelibly written into the annals of British railway accidents.

Another example of special service work occurred when, on the night of 31 January 1953, a massive storm with northerly gale-force winds struck a long stretch of coastline from the Humber down to the north Kent seaside resorts. In the ensuing tidal surge, sea defences were breached in hundreds of locations, allowing the North Sea to pour through into many areas of low-lying land on a scale never seen before. Over the worst hours of the storm and flooding, 307 persons died and it was

A remarkable escape by any standards. Here this glider has come to rest perched only on thin trees and live 400 volt electricity cables, after a lady pilot under instruction misjudged her landing approach. Firemen on one of the two ladders help the instructor to safety whilst other rescuers at the top of the electricity pole are about to release the unfortunate lady still in the cockpit. Note the lines around one wing and the tail section securing the precarious glider. The electricty cables have already been made safe. Both aviators made a complete recovery. Parham, Storrington, West Sussex. 27 January 1982 (John Craig)

A LUCKY ESCAPE

Jokes about lady learner-drivers are of course legion but one rarely, if ever, hears about the problems encountered by female aircraft pilots under instruction. West Sussex firemen were called to a glider crash on 27 January 1982 that involved just such a situation and fortunately this story has a happy ending.

In this unusual incident which took place at the Southern Gliding Club, Parham, firemen rescued the two occupants, an instructor and female pupil, from a glider which had crashed into the branches of a tree and come to rest suspended and finely balanced on overhead electric cables carrying 400 volts.

The power supply had to be turned off before rescue attempts could be made. Using ladders, up-to-the-minute cutting equipment and a hydraulic platform, the gliding instructor was helped out uninjured. His pupil was given first aid by fire crews in the cockpit of the glider before she was brought to ground level, using the hydraulic platform.

The sequel to this accident came several weeks later when the woman pupil, Mrs Gwen Brown, had recovered from her ordeal. She wrote to the West Sussex County Fire Officer, Robert Blackburn, to thank him personally for the care and attention given to her by her rescuers. But she also included an open letter of thanks to all the fire crews involved, which was duly forwarded to all the fire stations that had attended the glider crash.

In this letter Mrs Brown wrote:

Dear knights in yellow helmets – thank you! On Wednesday 27 January 1982 you were called to Parham Airfield, near Storrington, to rescue a maiden and her companion in distress from the treetops and a few electrical cables. I am the maiden, and thank you and God that I am still around to tell the tale.

At the time I could not appreciate the problems you were having in getting me down from the glider, just very glad to have you there to help me. I am now at home and slowly recovering from the ordeal. I am writing to thank you for your marvellous actions in bringing me back down to good old mother earth.

It is normal for people like myself to take for granted the emergency services we have in this country until the moment when we need them ourselves. Only then do we realise what a fantastic job you all do. No longer will my family and I take you for granted. Your colleague who spoke to me while I was still in the glider and after, descending via the hydraulic platform, made me feel calm, relaxed and thankful that I was alive, which I am sure helped me through the rest of the ordeal to come that day.

On seeing the photographs a few days later of the precarious position of the glider, I realised how difficult it was to rescue my instructor and me and all I can say to you is – I think you are wonderful.

necessary to evacuate over 30,000 from their homes. Homes, industrial and commercial premises, and public services alike were affected. Damage was so widespread that hundreds of miles of road and railway line were impassable, while many thousands of farm animals were lost in the flooded fields. It was as though the whole eastern and southeastern edge of the coastline was being reclaimed by the sea.

Fire brigades in the immediately affected areas were Lincolnshire (Lindsey and Kesteven brigades), Norfolk, Norwich, Great Yarmouth, Suffolk and Ipswich, Essex, Southend-on-Sea and Kent. Firemen from these brigades responded very quickly as the storm and the rising floodwater brought the first '999' calls for help. Before very long, these localised resources, many of them retained or part-time crews, were heavily committed effecting rescues, undertaking pumping-out work or assisting in the evacuation of a community where necessary.

It soon became obvious that a co-ordinated fire-service reinforcement into the affected areas was desirable. A regionalised structure of command primarily designed for wartime, or for precisely such national emergencies as the flooding, was available to the Home Office; consequently a number of brigades well removed from the affected area were asked to assist by providing crewed appliances to proceed to the stricken East Coast in convoy. Very soon, fire brigades from as far apart as Glamorgan and the West Riding of Yorkshire were mobilising a number of crews in what became known as 'Operation Seawall'.

But probably the greatest single factor that influenced the growth of fire-service rescue work was the opening of Britain's first motorway, the M1. On 2 November 1959 some 66 miles (106km) of new high-speed concrete carriageway was opened northwards from the outskirts of London, and for the first time motorists could potentially speed to and from the Midlands at an uninterrupted pace.

It was not long before the fears expressed by the fire service about the complications of possible major accidents on the M1 materialised. The new road had been open for only four months when a 39-vehicle pile-up spread itself between Junctions 9 and 10 on the Hertfordshire/Bedfordshire border. The accident happened during a particularly bad spell of thick fog which was so dense that fire appliances responding to '999' calls to the accident were forced to proceed at little more than walking pace with a fireman running cautiously in front waving a torch! Several motorists were killed and a dozen seriously injured in this first major motorway crash, and many of the casualties were released from their crushed vehicles by fire crews.

Before very long motorway accidents, particularly those involving many vehicles and a relatively large number of casualties, began to be a feature of the rescue work of fire brigades whose area was crossed by the new road. The low-lying fog of some parts of the South Midlands was a specially unwelcome hazard on the new motorway.

The 1960s brought a major special-service call to shipping. At 09.11 hours on Saturday 18 March 1967, the super-tanker *Torrey Canyon*, loaded with 119,000 tons (121,000 tonnes) of Kuwait crude oil bound for Milford Haven, went aground on a reef between the Isles of Scilly and Land's End. The *Torrey Canyon* was a huge vessel, only 50ft (15m) or so shorter in length than the *Queen Elizabeth*. The threat of oil pollution was on a scale which had no precedent anywhere in the world.

A CHEMICAL CHASE

Special services involving toxic chemical leaks and spillages are generally on the increase, but occasionally one occurs that taxes the resources of all concerned.

Such an unusual chemical incident took place in 1987, and involved a Dutch tanker which had disembarked from a ferry. Unknown to its driver, the tanker was leaking its contents as it sped to its destination. It trailed its leaking load of toxic liquid across West Sussex and Surrey before police finally stopped it on the M25.

By then, twelve people, including the tanker driver, seven police officers, two adults and two children were in hospital with eye and nose inflammation. Fortunately, none suffered lasting effects. It took the specialist skills of Surrey Fire Brigade and quite a sizable evacuation of the locality before the area was finally declared safe some hours after.

Abbeystead Water Works in Lancashire was the scene of a huge underground explosion in which fifteen visitors died. Here one of many firemen in breathing apparatus prepares to descend into the darkness of one of the flooded underground chambers to search for casualties. The large suction hose going into the shaft is pumping water out and is further restricting the already confined access for rescuers. 23 May 1984 (Lancashire Fire Brigade)

Within forty-eight hours, over 30,000 tons (30,500 tonnes) of oil had spilled out of the ship's ruptured holds and most of the black mass was heading for the beaches of Cornwall.

By this time, the government had ordered all possible assistance to the West Country to fight the incoming black tide with detergent sprays and mechanical clearance methods. Through the Home Office, regional support groups were mobilised and, very soon, huge convoys of government reserve fire pumps – Green Goddesses – were heading for the South West. So as not to diminish local fire-cover levels, some forty-three separate brigades were involved in providing crews of firemen volunteers. Every brigade found the response

The scene on the M6 at Fulwood, near Preston, of Britain's worst motorway crash. An intense fire following a collision between a coach and a number of cars and vans has been extinguished and all living casualties removed to hospital. Firemen now work in conjunction with police and ambulance colleagues to release the fatalities in several of the vehicles involved. Thirteen people died in this accident. Motorway and other traffic crashes nowadays form very much part of the regular rescue work of the fire service. 21 October 1985 (Lancashire Fire Brigade)

Another instance of a crash scene. Firemen inspect the aftermath of a mobile crane that has collided with several parked cars. Fortunately, there were no serious injuries. Hendon, North London. 6 January 1987 (London Fire Brigade)

from all ranks in the service overwhelming. It seemed as though everyone wanted to go to the aid of the stricken beaches.

Another very serious early motorway accident took place on the M1 in Bedfordshire on the morning of 16 March 1972. In the swirling fog, firemen released many casualties trapped in the impacted wreckage of lorries and cars continuously strewn over a mile (1.6km) of both carriageways. Eight people died and 53 were seriously injured in this worst-yet motorway accident. Several tankers carrying toxic chemicals were amongst the vehicles involved. The contents of one of these had spilt from the ruptured tanker and caught fire, adding to the difficulties of the hundred firemen at the scene.

Air transport provides a further example of crash rescue work. On a Sunday afternoon in July 1972, a BEA Trident aircraft bound for Brussels with 109 passengers and nine crew on board, crashed into a field immediately alongside the busy Staines bypass, only minutes after take-off from London's Heathrow Airport. There were no survivors and at that time the accident became Britain's worst air disaster. It was unfortunate that soon after the crash, radio stations broadcast the news and very many motorists in the area flocked to the crash scene, hindering and delaying firemen trying to get to the accident.

On the evening of 23 May 1984, Lancashire fire crews were called by the '999' system to an explosion at

RESCUES IN ALL SHAPES AND SIZES

A half-ton dolphin which had become stranded on Lowestoft beach by an exceptionally high tide gave Lowestoft firemen some difficult moments in January 1972. The crews succeeded in getting the animal on to a lorry which was then driven to the yacht club, where the dolphin was carefully launched down the slipway into calm water. After a couple of recuperative laps around the harbour, it made out to sea, none the worse for its brush with the fire service.

In the same month there came a very uncommon special service incident which fully engaged the skill and resourcefulness of the Staffordshire and Stoke-on-Trent Fire Brigades when twenty-six people were marooned high up in ten overhead cable cars at Trentham Pleasure Gardens. The cars had stopped quite suddenly at heights up to 40ft when one of them jumped off the haulage cable and became jammed against a supporting column.

Because of this, it was not possible to move any of the cars and, due to the dense nature of the trees and undergrowth all along the cable car ride, it was impossible to employ a hydraulic platform to get beneath each car to lift out the stranded passengers, many of whom were young children.

Using 45ft ladders and rescue lines, firemen ascended to each car, where one climbed inside to assure and comfort the distraught occupants. The derailed car first had to be lashed to secure it to the cable supports, and as the 45ft ladders were carefully pitched to each swinging cable car, the passengers were gently eased and assisted down to safety, each with a safety line tied to them and preceded down the ladder by a fireman.

All twenty-six persons were rescued in an arduous and delicate operation that lasted for three and a half hours. One woman was taken to hospital suffering from shock but was not detained.

the North West Waterworks at Abbeystead. Forty persons were reported to be injured. Two pumping appliances, an emergency tender and a divisional officer were immediately mobilised by fire control.

Abbeystead is a small village approached for some distance by winding lanes. Upon their arrival, crews were confronted by many casualties with a range of injuries and burns. Whilst most of these people were close to the building, others had wandered off into the surrounding fields. All were in a state of severe shock. Two ambulance crews were already in attendance, aided by people from the immediate neighbourhood who had heard the sound of the explosion.

In making a rapid assessment of the situation, the divisional officer established that an explosion had occurred in the building used as a valve house, during a visit by local residents. It had dislodged a number of concrete roof beams, each some 2½ tons (tonnes), which had then fallen into the valve house, trapping and injuring people there. Many had been able to stagger to open air but those remaining were either trapped or seriously injured.

Firemen were able to rescue eight persons in the early stages, but it was necessary to pump water out of all the underground chambers before firemen in breathing apparatus could descend into the tunnels and pipework of the complex. This was an extremely taxing task in claustrophobic conditions. Fifteen people died, and 23 were injured in this tragedy.

Very often, a fire-brigade special service takes place in a blaze of national publicity, and so it was in the early hours of 12 October 1984 at the Grand Hotel, Brighton, at the end of the Conservative Party conference. Virtually all the Cabinet was in residence when a huge bomb exploded, causing the collapse of parts of the upper floors down into the foyer area of the hotel. Many people were buried amid tons of compacted debris. Apart from the many casualties who were able to get themselves out in the subsequent lengthy rescue operation, the fire service managed to save nine residents and recover the bodies of four fatalities, although this was an extraordinarily protracted rescue mission.

During the early stages, fire-fighters made their way carefully over and through the debris, some of which was dangerously unstable. The search and rescues from the upper floors were particularly hazardous, with parts of the bomb-damaged building threatening further collapse as the rescuers went about their harrowing task. The Prime Minister subsequently wrote to Chief Fire Officer Whittaker of East Sussex Fire Brigade saying:

> The speed of response, the skill of operation, and above all, the magnificent courage of the Fire Service in working in conditions of great and growing danger

The rail crash scene at Clapham Junction several hours after three rush hour trains collided killing 35 passengers and seriously injuring 46 others. British Rail heavy lifting gear has joined in the rescue efforts of many London fire-fighters and medical teams to free those still trapped in the impacted wreckage of the three trains. Note the crushed carriage in the centre of the wreckage where many of the fatalities occurred. 12 December 1988 (Derek Robinson)

Clapham Junction – a further close up view of one of the most severely damaged carriages involved in the crash, giving some idea of the extrication task facing London fire-fighters. Note the rescue equipment in use, including high powered hydraulic metal cutting and spreading gear. 12 December 1988 (Derek Robinson)

following the bomb explosion in Brighton has been the subject of universal admiration.

I am writing to ask you to pass on my personal appreciation to all those involved for their devoted and selfless professionalism to which some of my closest colleagues and friends owe their lives. Just as we are saddened by the wickedness of people responsible for outrages of this sort, the example set by your men is an example and inspiration to the nation as a whole.

More recent large-scale special services have included the collision of three rush hour trains near Clapham Junction, south London, on 12 December 1988. Thirty-seven people were killed in the tragedy and the rescue of many survivors trapped in the crushed carriages of the packed trains gave London fire-fighters a daunting task.

And before the new year was very old, the crash of a British Midland Boeing 737 on the M1 motorway near Kegworth, Leicestershire, on 8 January 1989 following an engine fire could have been even more disastrous. Although 47 passengers lost their lives, fire crews cut free many of the 79 survivors.

(Right) The remains of what was Newnham House, Putney, South London, after a massive gas explosion demolished a large section of these flats. Several residents are unaccounted for and presumed buried and a carefully controlled rescue operation is under way. The danger to the firemen from the remaining unsafe structure is obvious. 10 January 1985 (London Fire Brigade)

(Overleaf) The aftermath of the terrorist bombing of the Grand Hotel, Brighton during the 1984 Conservative Party conference. High up on the fifth floor frontage, firemen gingerly search the unstable wreckage for more casualties. Note the safety lines around both firemen and several vertical steel support props literally holding up part of the sixth floor above. 12 October 1984 (Evening Argus)

10 OF RESCUE BOLD

As the earlier chapters of this book have shown, rescue was not the immediate priority for firemen of old. However, by the mid-nineteenth century the rescue of persons trapped by fire and smoke had become the primary task of fire-fighters. Unfortunately, detailed records of individual and multiple fire rescues carried out by olden-day firemen are rather sparse until just before World War I. Nevertheless, one such classic early multiple rescue that was duly recorded took place at the Carlton Hotel, Piccadilly in central London on 9 August 1911.

A serious fire on the first floor had developed during the early hours of the morning, and about a dozen guests were trapped above the fire at windows and on ledges. Some were threatening to jump. Firemen of the London Fire Brigade were on the scene within three minutes of the alarm being given and they immediately went to work. Unfortunately, the only access to the face of the hotel where people were imperilled by the fire was down a narrow courtyard. This made quite impossible any

An amazing wartime rescue of a woman, conscious and buried up to her neck, in the rubble of a house demolished by a V1 flying bomb. The fireman closest to the woman holds her hand whilst other rescuers dig carefully. An oxygen breathing apparatus set is close by if needed. The woman was extricated after two hours and made a complete recovery. Whitta Road, Manor Park, East London. 11 November 1944 (London Fire Brigade)

rescue attempt using wheeled escape ladders, or the new hand-operated turntable ladder.

But a dramatic rescue bid was mounted with four firemen using hook-ladders to get up to the trapped and screaming hotel residents. Hook-ladders were made of ash, 13ft (4m) long and only 10in (25cm) wide. By pitching them up floor by floor, and allowing the long steel hook at the ladder head to bear down on any projection, or at worst to be pushed through the glazing of a window, the ladder could provide a means, albeit somewhat unsteady, for a fireman to independently ascend the face of a building, floor by floor. Thus it was at the Carlton Hotel that night. By taking lowering ropes with them, the team of firemen quickly climbed up to all the trapped persons, several of whom were on ledges at sixth-floor level.

Although many other fire-fighters were tackling the fire below, the whole rescue operation took place amid swirling smoke and, of course, darkness. However, everyone was brought safely down by hook-ladder which in itself was quite a courageous feat, not only as regards the firemen concerned but those rescued as well. Unfortunately, six other residents died in the fire, the cause of which was never determined.

Non-fire rescues had grown in number and variety by the mid-1960s and firemen were turning their skills to any situation. But on 21 October 1966, a disaster of truly horrifying proportions befell the small south Wales valley community of Aberfan – one which was to tax the immediate response of the fire service to the utmost. At about 09.00 hours on that misty morning, a coal tip containing millions of tons of wet slurry started to slide down the hill above the village, and within minutes had engulfed Pantglas Junior School in its path and eighteen houses in adjoining Moy Road.

By 09.30 hours the first organised help arrived in the shape of two water tenders of Merthyr Tydfil County Borough Fire Brigade. The task facing the firemen was overwhelming. Where there had once been a school and rows of terraced houses was now a black, still slowly moving, mountain of coal slurry that had literally flattened everything in its path as it smashed its way down the hillside and into the centre of Aberfan village below. But as local word of the disaster spread, and even as the fire service was effecting the first rescues of child and adult buried up to their necks in the morass and rubble, more help was arriving, help that was soon to turn into a positive flood of men, particularly miners from the working shift at the nearby colliery, many of whom had children at the school.

Glamorgan County Fire Service assistance was also soon on the scene to aid the resources of the small Merthyr County Borough Brigade, and within an hour of the slurry avalanche, a massive digging operation was

well under way. Sadly, after 11.00 hours that same morning, no further live casualties were ever dug out, although the operation to search and locate the many missing children and adults went on for seven more days and nights. By then the fire-service contribution, apart from a number of initial rescues, included technical advice, provision of lighting, a water supply and canteens and, of course, the ready strength and expertise of hundreds of fireman, many of whom went to Aberfan as part of a vast reinforcement exercise involving brigades as far apart as Swansea, Newport and rural west Wales.

In all, 116 children and 28 adults died at Aberfan. It was in all respects an immense tragedy. Even today, officers and firemen who attended and saw at first hand the awful scene on that dreadful day in October 1966, are understandably reluctant to recall the horrors of Aberfan and Pantglas School.

Over the next decade, despite some dramatic rescues carried out by firemen at a spate of large London hotel fires between 1969 and 1971, it was the regular and growing motorway and other road crashes that seemed to engage the attention of television, radio and the press. However, this was somewhat redressed by the national media attention given to yet another large London hotel fire just before Christmas 1974. This incident was the capital's largest fire that year.

The horror of Aberfan, about two hours after the huge slide of coal slurry has engulfed Pantglas Junior School in the right foreground. A massive rescue operation is underway. 21 October 1966 (Western Mail)

At about 03.15 hours on Friday 13 December, an arsonist lit two separate fires on different floor levels of the Worsley Hotel, Clifton Gardens, Maida Vale. At the time the premises, a large five-storey Victorian terraced building, was being used as hotel staff accommodation. About 150 people were resident at the time. Despite an inadequate fire alarm system, the London Fire Brigade were at the scene only minutes after the first of many '999' calls. The chaos facing those first firemen was terrible. Semi-naked residents were fleeing the building, yet loud screams for help from the upper floors pinpointed about thirty persons at windows and actually out on narrow ledges who had not been able to make their escape because of the thick smoke spreading up staircases from the fires below.

Reinforcing crews were already arriving at the escalating incident even as the first rescues were being perilously carried out by those firemen first on the scene. Using wheeled escapes, extension ladders, turntable ladders and hook-ladders, the fire-fighters began to scale the Worsley Hotel both front and back as fire was breaking through windows all around. These multiple rescues were not made easy by the double-parked cars all along the hotel frontage which impeded the positioning of all the ladders in use.

The first jets of water were trained on the frontage

The dramatic rescue of firemen by firemen. About an hour after surrounding a large fire at the Worsley Hotel in London's Maida Vale, four firemen were trapped when part of the hotel roof suddenly fell in. The battle to extricate the trapped men lasted over three hours whilst the fire raged all around. Here, the first of those buried is released. He is coming out of the window head-first on the back of another fireman (the centre of the top three on ladders). Of the four casualties, one died and two were seriously burnt. Note severe fire damage to hotel frontage. The fire was caused by an arsonist. The author is on the extreme left of the topmost group of firemen. 13 December 1974 (London Fire Brigade)

of the hotel to cool the first firemen from the intense radiated heat as they ascended their ladders to the trapped persons. One dramatic rescue followed another, as firemen coaxed and cajoled the imperilled and frightened groups onto their ladders and then down to safety. More and more men and appliances were arriving in response to urgent radio requests, and inside 15 minutes about 70 firemen and 20 fire-engines were engaged in the battle.

Then, once all the visible rescues had been successfully completed before anyone jumped, the battle to contain the spreading fire began in earnest. Firemen on all sides slowly worked together to surround the thunderous, roaring inferno that had now broken out through the roof of the hotel. Inside the building, two stone staircases had collapsed very early on, and crews in breathing apparatus who were penetrating that part of the hotel with jets had first to rig ladders over the gaping voids in order to pursue the fiery mass funnelling up the stairwell above. Conditions inside the hotel were dangerous and uncomfortable, and firemen had to contend with a rapidly worsening situation involving remote parts of the building as fire spread along corridors and up the lift-shafts and staircases to the floors above.

After about an hour, as crews from many stations worked off ladders and up staircases to the heart of the

Another view of drama at the Worsley Hotel. Station Officer Colin Searle of Westminster Fire Station is stretchered to an ambulance after being partially buried in hot brickwork for almost two hours. He recovered from his ordeal, in which he suffered extensive burns to both legs and subsequently returned to operational duties after many months of specialised hospital care (London Fire Brigade)

An unusual and dangerous rescue seventeen floors up a building site tower crane. The crane driver was badly injured and trapped in his control cabin after part of the crane above crashed down, killing another workman. Firemen had first to rig ladders to get up to the casualty, and the task of getting him to safety at ground level was complicated and protracted as can be seen from the photograph. Norland Road, North Kensington, West London. 28 January 1968 (London Fire Brigade)

fire, a sudden collapse of part of the hotel roof occurred. The fire-weakened structure crashed into the room below and this floor, also weak through fire damage to the joists, gave way. The entire smoking and flaming mass fell into room No 13 on the second floor, burying a station officer and three firemen who were working a jet there. When the outside firemen nearest to the collapse scrambled up a ladder to the front window of the smoking room, only two of the trapped crew were initially visible. Both were conscious but in obvious pain and were buried chest-high by the fall. The whereabouts of the third fireman was soon discovered amid the piled and smoking debris in the tiny room when he waved his hand out of the impacted timbers. He was almost totally buried. All the trapped men were in danger of being slowly roasted alive from the burning fires in the debris in which they were trapped.

Rescue teams very quickly set to work to free the helpless men and dug with their bare hands at the hot bricks and massive wooden beams. Indeed, firemen were now faced with a rescue of a different sort – fireman now dug for fireman, friend for friend, mate for mate. And to add to the hazards within the tiny room, choking smoke and steam made it almost impossible at times for the rescue teams to see what they were doing, and frequent falls from the dislodged brickwork and still-

Suffer little children. Two firemen resuscitating a child overcome by smoke in a dwelling fire in Southwark, South London. 10 December 1971 (Owen Rowland)

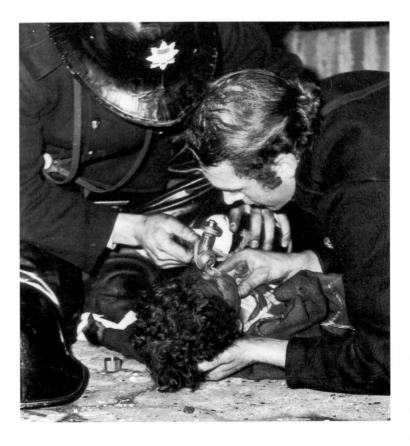

burning timbers above added urgency to the entire operation.

Following one and a half hours of sheer dogged determination by the rescue teams in the most dreadful conditions in that room, the first two trapped firemen were finally extricated, brought down to street level and rushed to hospital, both badly burned and injured. The rescue of the third fireman was a more difficult task because of the sheer weight of debris upon him. Sadly, as his rescuers toiled, swore, coughed and spluttered amid the swirling gloom, they discovered the lifeless form of another fireman buried even deeper. This was a young probationer-fireman of only eight months' service named Hamish Pettit, and when he was extricated from the collapse some time later – the last of the four-man crew to be freed – he was certified dead on the spot by a doctor from the St Mary's Hospital medical team who had come to the fire scene soon after the collapse took place.

Although six bodies were subsequently recovered from deep inside the building, the rescue of over thirty residents from great peril in the early stages of the fire was a great achievement by all those firemen concerned. Only in the closing stages of the incident did the fire seemingly reassert itself and bring death and injury to the rescuers themselves.

The Worsley Hotel fire epitomised the very dangerous and demanding world of fire-fighting and it was significant that in due course twenty-two London firemen of various ranks were commended by their chief fire officer for their actions at the fire and during the later rescues of the trapped fire-fighters. Several months later, eight of the twenty-two were honoured by Her Majesty the Queen with the award of Queen's Gallantry Medals and Queen's Commendations for Brave Conduct. One of the latter honours went posthumously to Fireman Hamish Pettit for his hook-ladder rescue before the disastrous roof collapse of that fateful Friday the 13th which wrote another chapter of fire service history.

Then, only two months later, another huge rescue operation involving the London Fire Brigade transfixed the entire nation's attention for five days and nights – Moorgate.

At the peak of the morning rush hour on 28 February 1975, at about 08.46 hours, a six-carriage tube train crowded with incoming London commuters failed to slow down for its last stop at the Moorgate terminus, ploughed through the sand-drag and buffer stops and slammed into the wall inside the dead-end of the tunnel. The front three carriages concertinaed and in a few horrifying seconds many men and women were crushed to death. Other passengers in the packed confines of the front carriages clung perilously to life despite serious injuries and being jammed into tortuous positions, often

SEEING THROUGH SMOKE

One of the great techno-logical developments of recent years has been the introduction of thermal imaging cameras. These enable fire-fighters literally to see through smoke and to identify not only the seat of fires deep inside buildings but also to show the outline of casualties who have collapsed after being overcome by smoke. The cameras are, however, rather bulky and are expensive.

Soon after their intro-duction, it became clear that these cameras would also be of use in locating casualties trapped under the debris of collapsed buildings at non-fire incidents such as gas explosions, and so it has proved to be. Such is the expertise of the fire service today using thermal imaging cameras that London firemen have travelled with their sophisticated equipment to Mexico in 1985 and to El Salvador one year later, following the huge earthquakes in those countries.

The London Transport Moorgate tube disaster in which 42 passengers were killed and 76 injured when a rush-hour train crashed at speed into a dead-end tunnel. Here one of many fire crews at the scene inch their way slowly forwards on the roof of the second carriage of the train. In front of the firemen is the compacted first coach partly crushed up against the tunnel roof. 28 February 1975. (London Fire Brigade)

beneath or alongside inert yet warm bodies. Upon the tremendous impact of the crash, all the lighting in the train and on the platform went out and the whole area was clouded in thick black dust. Fortunately, no fire broke out.

When the first brigade appliances arrived soon after the crash, the enormous scale of the tragedy and the task ahead became clear, and the officer in charge of the first crews initiated 'major accident procedure'. In accordance with the prearranged plan, fire appliances, ambulances and police cars were summoned from all over central London, and nearby hospitals put on full alert.

Fortunately, the rear three carriages of the train were quickly cleared of blackened and dazed casualties, and a mass assault was mounted to free the many people trapped in the front part of the train. The crushed and tangled red metalwork of the carriages seemed to fill the 70ft (21m) long dead-end tunnel, and initially only one fireman at a time could wriggle into the wreck through holes cut in a carriage end-panels and roofs, or by worming his way up the narrow sides of the tunnel and into the train through the shattered windows. As the firemen crawled into the carriages, they saw in the light of their powerful torches that a number of people were already beyond help, although many others were trapped, injured but conscious. Afterwards, many of the survivors said that once they saw the firemen coming through the wreckage towards them they knew they would get out alive. Sadly, not all the injured did.

All the firemen's power-cutting equipment, crowbars, hacksaws and many other tools had to be passed into the train by the same difficult path. As morning wore on, the live casualties were released one by one and manhandled back down through the train and out to the platform where the ambulance service took them the short journey to hospital. All the firemen were going into the wreckage on a short 'work and relief' system, and crews stripped to the waist and worked like Trojans in the ever-deteriorating conditions. They worked under and amongst tons of hanging and mangled metal and slowly penetrated further and further into the mass, but progress seemed excruciatingly slow.

A surgical team from a nearby hospital had earlier set up its equipment on the platform, and doctors frequently crawled into the wreckage to give drugs to a victim while firemen worked on undaunted. By mid-morning, twenty-five trapped passengers had been extricated, although about forty were still pinned in the crumpled front two carriages. Flood-lighting had now been provided inside the wreckage and on the platform, and steady progress in the work of extrication was made. Fresh relief crews took over from the grimy night-shift of firemen still on the scene, as more and more men and appliances arrived at Moorgate. By noon, seventy casualties had been removed, but heat continued to build up to add to the discomfort of those still trapped and their toiling rescuers. Working in temperatures of over 100°F (38°C) the firemen sweated away, cutting, bending and lifting the twisted metal and timber of the carriages. Continually, with a quiet and reassuring word, they comforted the passengers who were still trapped.

After many hours of grimy and stomach-turning work, around mid-afternoon it became evident that only two of those still trapped in the train were alive. One of these, a young City of London policewoman, was hopelessly caught by her foot. Only after there had been a valiant struggle to free her did the doctors decide that drastic steps must be taken. A crew of firemen supported the woman whilst a surgical team amputated her foot at the ankle. She was then gently carried back through the carriages, and an hour later the last live casualty, a young man, was finally released.

Then began the sad task of retrieving the many bodies still entombed amid the wreckage. Over the next three days and nights, teams of firemen worked to recover them, while the air in the tunnel became progressively more fetid. The fire crews had to wear filtered masks and gloves as they struggled to free the crushed forms. Later on, the atmosphere in the tunnel of death became so putrid that firemen had to don

A moment of rescue. After an hour of struggle, a construction site worker is hoisted to safety after being partly buried in a deep trench. Note the drip and oxygen supply set up by the medical team present, and the sheer intensity of the operation which is being closely covered by a TV news camera. Fortunately the casualty survived. 17 June 1986 (West Midlands Fire Service)

Animals often lead to protracted rescue operations. Here a pony who has become stuck in deep mud is pulled to safety after a two-hour struggle by firemen to get strops around the unfortunate animal. Wolverhampton, West Midlands. 27 January 1987 (Wolverhampton Express and Star)

breathing apparatus and any direct contact with a body meant a full decontamination shower and a fresh set of clothes. Even the tiniest scratch necessitated an anti-tetanus injection, for the medical advisers present were growing increasingly worried about the health hazard to the rescuers. By the fourth morning after the crash, all firemen entering the train had first to change their own uniforms for dungarees and rubber boots that were then completely cleansed after a crew had been relieved.

As each piece of wreckage was finally cleared of bodies, it was winched out of the dead-end tunnel by railway engineers. The last and final body, that of the driver of the train, was recovered on the evening of 5 March. Over 1,000 London firemen had been in attendance over the five days and four nights following the Moorgate crash, and the final toll stood at 42 dead and 76 persons injured.

The Chief Officer of the London Fire Brigade at the time was Joe Milner, who described his Moorgate rescue crews in the *London Evening News* as 'my thousand selfless heroes'. Surely no more apposite tribute to those fireman could have been made.

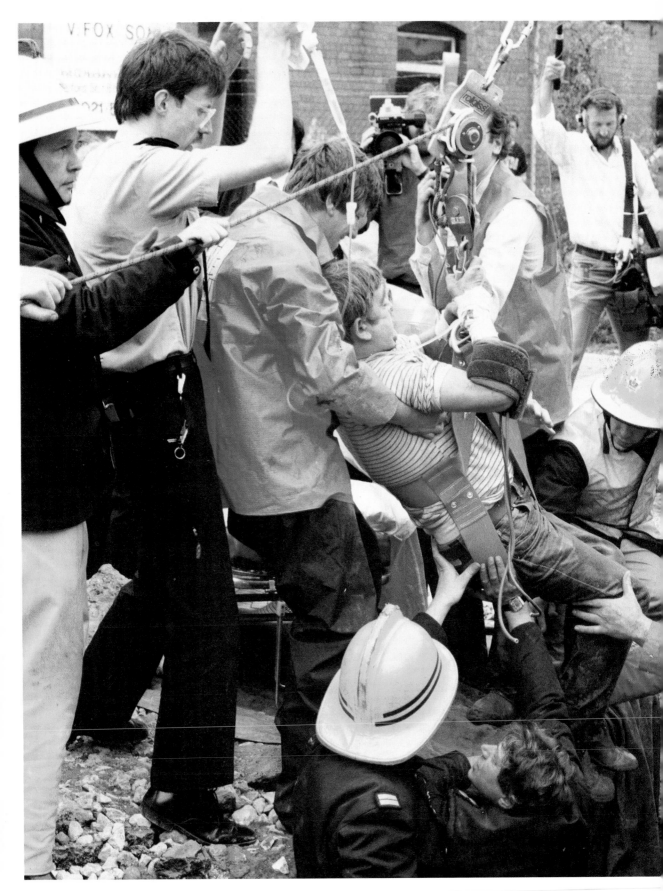

11 MODERN FIRE-FIGHTERS

THE INSTITUTION OF FIRE ENGINEERS

This body was founded in 1918 by several prominent Chief Fire Officers to provide a national organisation for the furtherance of fire fighting techniques, fire prevention understanding and the education of those involved in such work.

Today, the Institution of Fire Engineers (IFE) has a unique place in the modern-day structure of fire defence. It has 9,500 members not only in the United Kingdom but in twenty-one countries world-wide, and its annual examinations have for many years been a reciprocal part of the uniformed fire service promotion path. The IFE membership is drawn not only from fire service personnel but also from the world of architecture and building design, insurance and fire equipment manufacturers.

There is an extensive network of home and overseas branches, each active through seminars, meetings and visits. The IFE also produces regular technical fire publications together with a quarterly journal and is represented on a number of national committees dealing with many aspects of fire-fighting and fire safety matters.

The fire stations of today's British fire service are, as we have seen, manned either by professional fire-fighters or by volunteers known as 'retained firemen' where the likelihood of fire is fairly low, such as in the rural areas of the country.

Professional firemen are recruited between the ages of eighteen and thirty. There is only a single-tier entry to fire brigades and hence all chief fire officers and senior officers come through the ranks. Recruits therefore arrive direct from school, college and, occasionally, from university, as well as from jobs as diverse as engineering, the retail trade and banking. Very many of today's recruits seek a physical challenge, excitement and job satisfaction that was not present in their previous employment. Few are disappointed. Annual wastage from the fire service is minimal, with virtually all retirements being on age – on or around fifty-five years – or on medical grounds often through injury gained during operational action.

Full-time recruit fire-fighters undertake an intensive fourteen-week basic training course. During the course, which is usually of a residential nature, great emphasis is continually placed on a host of physical skills and theoretical knowledge, the aim being to bring about complete competence with a fire-fighter's weaponry of pumps, hoses, ladders, breathing apparatus, extinguishers and cutting gear.

The course also instils discipline into a recruit and will certainly exorcise any reluctance to work at great heights or in claustrophobic conditions. It will quickly engender the spirit of teamwork and pride of service that is so much part of a fireman's life, yet sadly a very small number of young recruits do not survive the physical rigours of the first few days. The discipline is often too austere, particularly if these youngsters have come from backgrounds where they have not experienced such demands on their bodies and minds.

Once the course is completed, a recruit is posted to an operational fire station to begin a two-year probationary period, following which progression can be made through three levels of national examination, both practical and theoretical, to promotion to the lower and middle ranks of the service.

Career progression beyond this level depends on personal ability and performance, with attendance on a

An aerial view of the massive tank fire at the Amoco Refinery, Milford Haven, Dyfed on 30 August 1983. The battle is on to prevent the fire spreading to many similar tanks just beyond. Many cooling jets are at work behind the smoke to protect the other tanks. It was 60 hours before the fire was brought under control by 200 firemen not only from Dyfed Brigade but from many adjacent counties. Extra foam was ferried to the scene under police escort from as far away as the West Midlands (Eye Level Photographs)

Another view of the burning oil tank showing the intensity and the buckling effect that the tremendous heat has had on the steel sides of the tank. This was one of the problems for fire-fighters in that had the tank ruptured, many thousands of escaping gallons would have formed a burning river to threaten all in its path. £10 million damage was caused but the refinery stayed in business. Amoco Refinery, Milford Haven, Dyfed. 30 August 1983 (Colin Kaijaks)

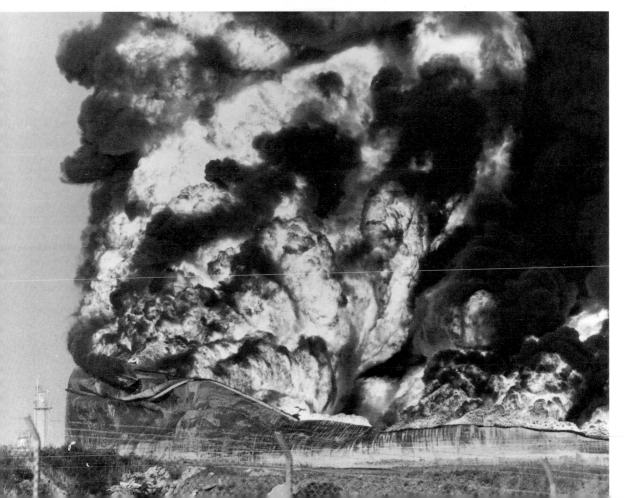

FUNERAL OF A HERO

One of the fatal casualties of the Kings Cross fire of 18 November 1987 was 45-year-old Station Officer Colin Townsley of Soho Fire Station. At the subsequent full brigade funeral, *The Times'* correspondent wrote:

No military rituals attend the deaths of firemen, no gun carriage bears them to their final rest. But yesterday the fire service put out its finest panoply of honour for the funeral of Station Officer Colin Townsley, who died attempting to save passengers in the Kings Cross Underground fire.

Rarely, it was said over his flag-draped coffin, would one fireman boast of his own or another's heroism to an outsider. Yesterday was an exception; some 3,000 firemen, representing every brigade in Britain, set aside their pride to give one of their number the fireman's equivalent of a state funeral.

His bier was a turntable ladder, dressed over-all in dozens of wreaths of white, red and yellow, dominated by the word 'Guv' picked out in white chrysanthemums, a last tribute from the men of Red Watch at ·Soho fire station who were a bare two hours into their shift when summoned to that fateful incident in which thirty others lost their lives in the fire, smoke and confusion of Kings Cross.

His coffin lay on the vehicle's platform beneath the ladder, draped with the Union flag, his white helmet and fire service long service and good conduct medal on a black cushion among the wreaths on top, and attended by six pallbearers from Red Watch, bare-headed and at stiff attention.

Before the ladder in convoy drove two black hearses full of wreaths sent from all over the world, and two flower-decked fire engines, one of them the actual vehicle that took Colin Townsley from Soho station to his last call, his seat in the cab left poignantly empty.

The funeral of a hero. The coffin of Station Officer Colin Townsley, who died whilst attempting to rescue trapped passengers in the smoke-filled booking hall at Kings Cross Underground Station, moves slowly through Soho en route to a full service funeral. The floral tributes came from every fire brigade in the UK and some even came from abroad. 27 November 1987 (London Fire Brigade)

The fire-fighter never knows what type of incident he will face next. Crews of West Yorkshire Fire Service check the tankers of a derailed petrol train inside Summit Tunnel under the Pennines. This part of the fire had been extinguished but deeper inside the tunnel tankers are still burning and there is a constant risk of explosion. 20 December 1984 (West Yorkshire Fire Service)

Road traffic crashes are certainly an expected part of a fireman's operational work. Here a team of four firemen in chemical protection suits and breathing apparatus stand by after a collision involving a liquid nitrogen tanker, another heavy lorry and a coach (on its side between the two other vehicles). There has been no fire but there is an explosion risk from the tanker's contents. Some hazardous substances are so toxic that fire crews have to wear an even higher level of protection than that shown. Note the '2RE 1977' panel on rear of damaged tanker. This provides firemen with much instant information as to the tanker contents and is part of an international marking scheme. M6 Motorway. 17 November 1985 (West Midlands Fire Service)

series of progressive courses at the Fire Service College at Moreton-in-Marsh in Gloucestershire. At this Home Office establishment a wide range of courses cater for command, management, scientific, technical and legal aspects of the fire service. The college has the finest range of purpose built fire-training buildings in the world, where many of a fire-fighter's real life hazards and situations can be created under controlled conditions. Indeed, the Cotswolds would seem to be the last place to find, amongst other features, high-rise flats, a sewer complex, chemical works, a section of motorway where realistic crashes are staged, and a full-scale concrete ship surrounded by water! The Fire Service College is a place of surprises.

Retained (part-time/volunteer) fire-fighters serving on rural fire stations are recruited from the community they serve, and are usually drawn from persons living or working within one mile (1.6km) of their local fire station. This is simply to facilitate a speedy turnout when their 'bleepers' go off and activate a frantic dash to man the appliance. Being a retained fireman frequently requires an understanding employer and family to cope with disturbances at all hours of the day and night. Apart from a basic training course, a retained fire-fighter is required to attend regular weekly drill-night sessions and occasional exercises and weekend activites, for

One of a fireman's tools of recent years – the thermal imaging camera. This device visually identifies differences in temperature and can pinpoint through thick smoke not only the seat of a fire but also persons trapped under rubble such as here after a gas explosion that has blown the wall of a house right out. These cameras were used to good effect by British firemen at Mexico City in 1984 after the earthquake there. Farleigh Road, Dalston, North London. 13 March 1987 (London Fire Brigade)

MEDIA REPORTING

One of the regular features of press, radio and television reporting of fires is their singular ability to misreport what has gone on during fire-fighting operations and thereafter. Very many firemen have great difficulty in relating a media report to the actual fire they attended but a few hours earlier. In some instances, reports neglect to mention that the fire service is even present. An MP summed up the situation several years back whilst staying at an hotel in Grays, Essex, when fire broke out:

What made me marvel was the speed, calm, precision and silence of the firemen. Each went about his allotted job and the man at whom I marvelled most had the job of walking first into the fire. Reconnaissance, we used to call it in the Army; the stickiest job of all. Half a dozen newspapers reported the fire and they all mentioned me. Reports of my behaviour in the crisis were more colourful than accurate. But I'm not complaining – the inaccuracies were all in my favour. The firemen, of course, weren't mentioned at all!

The press, in particular, has also invented a language and style all of their own when reporting fires. On regular occasions fire *rips, roars* or *tears through* a building, which then becomes *razed. gutted* or *burnt down*, despite the efforts of firefighters.

Even when firemen have saved two-thirds of a premises from fire spread through sweat and toil, the media report will emphasise that *one* third of the building was razed, gutted or burnt down! There hardly seems any justice in the matter – ask any fireman!

A scene from a fireman's daily training session. Here a 45ft ladder has been pitched to a training tower to allow for 'carry down' practice, a drill virtually unchanged over 100 years of fire brigades. Note, however, the safety harness and line securing the 'casualty' and the solid construction of the alloy ladder which is specially designed for fire service use (Devon Fire and Rescue Service)

which an annual sum is paid, in addition to payment for '999' turnouts and drill attendance.

In recent years, the first females to serve as fire-fighters have joined their male counterparts in several brigades, both full-time and retained, and although their collective numbers have remained very small, they have started a trend that has in part dispelled the impression that modern fire-fighting is an exclusively male domain.

Fire stations, both full-time and retained, are alerted to fire calls and other emergencies by central control rooms strategically sited within each fire-brigade territory. All '999' fire calls for a brigade's area will be routed here from British Telecom and other sources, and the mobilising of fire appliances and crews will be co-ordinated by uniformed operators. In despatching fire-fighters to incidents, control room staff will utilise computer-aided systems to determine whether a particular '999' call address warrants one appliance or three. This is determined by the fire risk category of the building involved under Home Office time-limit standards. A city centre address will attract up to three pumps and a high-rise turntable ladder at the scene inside eight minutes of the initial '999' call, whereas a fire call to a rural farm will require a minimal response of one pump inside twenty minutes. In practice, these rural attendance times are often well inside these limits.

This view shows two firemen undergoing training at Devon's Training School in both the wearing of gas-tight protection suits and their subsequent decontamination after coming into contact with a hazardous substance. As the instructor makes a point the water spray device ensures all traces of any harmful chemical are diluted and removed. Both firemen are wearing breathing apparatus inside their protective suits and by now will be very warm (Devon Fire and Rescue Service)

POWERS OF ENTRY

Firemen, when on duty and in uniform, have bestowed upon them, through the 1947 Fire Services Act, a unique and wide-ranging power of immediate entry into premises throughout the United Kingdom. This power in law obviously permits a fireman access into a building to put out a fire. Less well-known is the legal right he has to gain access to a fire *through* other premises not so affected, for the purpose of fire-fighting and mitigating the damage likely to be caused by fire.

In practice this means that a householder cannot deny a fireman access into his dwelling when hoses, ladders or flood-lighting need to be taken through to a fire at the rear of the building. Naturally enough, fire crews only use access through an unaffected property when it is essential for fire-fighting operations, and then take all due care to avoid unnecessary damage to fixtures and fittings in the mêlée of dealing with the fire before it spreads out of control.

Occasionally though, there is the odd mis-understanding of this fireman's legal power and its application at time of crisis. Paradoxically, such difficulties are usually only sorted out after some assistance from police officers, who have no similar right of entry without prior recourse to the courts!

Many firemen are active in fringe activities involving brigade sporting and social activities of the widest sort. In addition, several UK brigades support their own bands which provide music and ceremony for various events throughout the year. Here the Ceremonial Unit of Devon Fire and Rescue Service march down Queen Victoria Street, in the City of London, to commemorate a charity drive by an ex-Devon fire engine (at rear) from Norway to Africa. The Unit consists of a Corps of Drums and Bugles, a marching squad and a colour party. They are made up entirely of serving or retired members of the brigade and are widely acclaimed for their musical skills, drill standard and turnout. 3 November 1987 (Devon Fire and Rescue Service)

The central control rooms will also provide a whole wealth of back-up technical information to fire-fighters at the scene, and maintain radio links during the operation, be it a fire or a road crash with persons trapped. If unknown chemicals have fallen off a lorry or are spilt, control will inform the crews what personal protection and specialist action is needed. At a large incident, control staff will order on reinforcing appliances from available resources and provide back-up moves to maintain fire cover in the affected district.

When not attending operational incidents, fire-fighters spend the beginning of shift on-duty time checking vehicles and equipment to ensure their immediate availability, as well as taking part in daily drill sessions where ladders, pumps and breathing apparatus are utilised in dealing with a variety of 'mock' fire situations. Scrap cars are also carefully yet quickly cut apart in practice for real-life road accidents.

In addition to this training, operational crews have to be completely familiar with their 'patch'. They must regularly check hundreds of fire hydrants and also inspect small shops, business premises and schools for compliance with basic fire-safety requirements such as exits, extinguishers and fire alarms. Fire-fighters also have to spend part of their duty shift in arduous fitness training so necessary to keep in physical shape to face the demanding rigours of the job at day and night, in all weathers and at extremes of temperature.

Several small specialist uniformed groups also operate within the fire service, such as training instructors and fire-prevention officers. The latter group consists of personnel who – amongst other matters – undertake full-time advisory work on plans submitted for new buildings, produce fire-safety certificates for factories, hotels and boarding houses, and carry out liaison with local authorites and the police on licensed premises. In all, there are today fifty-seven different acts, statutes and regulations concerning fire safety. All fire-prevention officers have served time as operational firemen and thus know and appreciate the nature and behaviour of fire. Their work contributes to the fire-safety defence of the nation, helps to minimise fire losses, and in general is an unseen yet important part of the work of the modern-day fire service.

WOULD-BE RESCUERS

We are weary, sad at heart,
Never had a chance from start,
Far too late we got the call,
Gave us wrong address and all.

Broken in was large front door,
Giving vent to fire in store.
By the time we did arrive
No one there could be alive.

Child was found at head of stairs.
All the rest lay dead in pairs.
Can one say to those who try,
'Have you never reasoned why?' – Charles Clisby

APPETITES

During the huge fire at the Amoco Refinery at Milford Haven, Dyfed, West Wales, which started on 30 August 1983, a total of some 250 fire-fighters, including some from five other county brigades beside Dyfed, fought to prevent the fire burning in several oil tanks from spreading to the remainder of the huge oil refinery. The battle lasted for five days and nights before the firemen successfully gained control.

Feeding the hungry fire-fighters was a major logistical task in itself, and between 30 August and 4 September 1983, the following food was consumed at mobile feeding stations near to the oil refinery and its blazing tanks:

1,860 lbs chips
1,000 portions brown sauce
3,168 sausages
20 × 750g tins coffee
2,375 slices bacon
940 pints milk
906 pies
200 lbs sugar
2,520 eggs

Appetites indeed!

12 HOW SAFE?

It is a tragic fact that around 900 men, women and children have perished in fires in the United Kingdom in each recent year. By far the greatest number of these fatalities occur in the home, and many take place during the hours of darkness.

Direct fire losses, ie the measurable amount of material damage caused by fire, totals an annual sum of about £550 million. Much more difficult to quantify is indirect fire loss, covering such things as loss of potential orders through a factory fire and shut-down, and the cost of employee production time lost through the disruptive effects of fire in a business concern. Indirect fire loss is conservatively put at twice as much as the direct figure. Both annual sums show an upward trend every year even when inflation is taken into account, parallel to the steady increase over the past thirty years in the number of fire calls answered by firemen up and down the land. These now run at about 400,000 individual fires, large and small.

Fires of a £1 million loss were virtually unknown until the early 1920s, and even then were the result of a huge conflagration at a large commercial works. In today's technological world, a £1 million loss can result from a fairly small fire in many occupancies such as offices, shops and the smallest of factories where complex computerised equipment is extremely vulnerable to smoke, heat and flames. By today's standards, £1 million fires are fairly common occurrences, and every year there is usually a £50 million blaze. Even the £150 million fire-loss barrier has been broken in recent years.

Firemen today train many groups from the community in basic fire safety. Here a young lady home help looks on in awe as a leading fireman instructor burns wet paper inside a training building. He is preparing to demonstrate how to move low down in smoke to her and her social services colleagues (Devon Fire and Rescue Service)

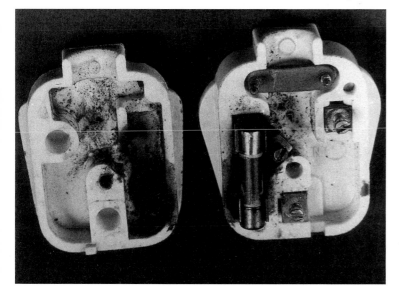

The cause of many fires. Here in this electrical plug is advance evidence of localised overheating, probably caused by an incorrectly fitted fuse link. Before many more hours this plug would have almost certainly caused a fire (London Fire Brigade)

The largest UK fire loss to date. The Ministry of Defence Army Central Ordnance Depot fire on 24 June 1983 at Donnington, Shropshire, that cost £165 million damage. Almost five years later, another huge fire in another warehouse on the same site caused £100 million loss (Fire Protection Association)

In the face of these steadily rising figures of death and destruction by fire, it is important to note that the fire service today puts in more effort to reduce fire losses than ever in its history. As mentioned in the previous chapter, the work of specialist uniformed fire-prevention officers relates to the implementation of the current fifty-seven fire-safety acts and statutes relating to factories, offices and other places such as hotels, large department stores, theatres and licensed premises, as well as the giving of goodwill fire-prevention advice to anyone who asks for it.

Operational firemen on fire stations also take on some fire-safety inspections in small commercial and business premises. In recent years, firemen have also been leading a drive to make householders more aware of the dangers from discarded cigarette ends, overloaded electrical circuits, unattended cooking stoves and the problems of young children playing with matches. Since the public has become aware of the deadly smoke threat from polyurethane foam furniture, domestic smoke alarms have taken on a new popularity and significance, largely due to fire-service publicity. It will be interesting to see whether in future years these devices have some effect on reducing the tragic death toll and injury from dwelling-house fires. In recent times, public information features during television peak hour periods have been

MORE FIRE-RAISING RATS

Amongst the causes of fire of the 1860s were several headings that would not be out of place today. Careless disposal of cigars, pipe-tobacco and matches; cooking left unattended, and defective chimney flues are all amongst modern regular causes of fire. However, rats are most certainly not, whereas in the nineteenth century such rodents were a significant cause of fire outbreak.

For some years rats had gnawed through lead water-piping to obtain a drink, but with the coming of piped gas to the capital there were numerous serious explosions caused by rats being unable to discriminate between water and gas pipes. Having gnawed through a gas pipe, the escaping gas soon found an ignition source.

Another problem with rats was their liking for the wax on lucifer sticks. Having consumed the wax, they would quite regularly gnaw into the phosphorus head of the lucifer, which would quickly ignite any adjacent materials, as well as cremating the rat.

FIRE IN THE HOME – THE FACTS

Every year there are about 50,000 accidental fires in homes which together kill and injure more than 6,500 people.

More than half those killed each year by fire are aged 60 or over, and many of these fatal fires occur at night.

Two major causes of fire in the home are:
(a) carelessly disposed cigarettes, matches and lighters igniting bedding and upholstery, and
(b) cooking accidents – there are about 15,000 chip pan fires every year.

Faulty or misused electrical equipment such as electric blankets, cookers, heaters and television sets account for another 26,500 domestic fires, of which 150 will cause fatalities.

It is an appalling catalogue of death and suffering on a wide scale. Almost all such cases could actually be avoided if some common sense fire safety rules were observed. Much free fire prevention publicity material is readily available from every fire station in the United Kingdom.

Whilst virtually all places of work or public entertainment are subject to stringent fire safety requirements, a home is not, and yet this is where the majority of fire deaths occur. Perhaps the day is not far away when a householder will be required to take some basic fire precautionary measures, such as the fitting of a single smoke alarm and a fire extinguisher.

Even a nightly check to see that all is well before retiring could one day save a family from thick black toxic smoke mushrooming up the stairs from a burning sofa in the lounge. No doubt open doors encourage the passage of the suffocating and blinding smoke upwards yet hopefully, someone will be aroused before yet more domestic fire casualties are asphyxiated in their sleep. It takes only two to three minutes for this awful scenario to develop before firemen arrive to confront the fiery situation, perhaps to carry out rescues if a family have not already escaped, or at worst, reverently recover their smoke-blackened bodies. 50,000 such fires a year is an awful and unacceptable indictment of the community at large, yet hopefully one day the survival message will get through.

Or will it?

Fire kills.
Think about it.

Prepared for the Home Office by the Central Office of Information 1984. Printed in the U.K. for H.M.S.O. J0085NJ Dd 8832773.

used to drive home the domestic fire-safety message, so far without any real reduction in such fires.

Places of work and public resort do, of course, require much more sophisticated fire-safety measures. Fire exits, means of escape, fire alarms, automatic fire and smoke detection systems, sprinklers, fire-fighting water mains at all floor levels of high-rise buildings, provision for firemen rapidly to utilise lifts to gain access to upper floors, hand fire-extinguishers and staff training in case of fire, are all part of today's organised and complex fire-safety defence of the community at both work and play. And all these measures are generally very costly to provide and to maintain, especially where there still exists the occasional attitude that says, 'fire cannot happen here'.

Fortunately, the fire service is not alone in promoting a safer world. The Loss Prevention Council (LPC) is the UK insurance technical organization involved with all aspects of loss prevention and control on a worldwide basis. The LPC is supported by the Association of British

Apart from regular inspections of fire exits and fire alarms, firemen also check extinguishers to ensure they are ready for immediate use. This fire point shows a number of foam extinguishers and sand buckets near to a flammable liquids store in a factory (Devon Fire and Rescue Service)

One of the most effective fire safety symbols ever, currently used throughout the British Fire Service as part of its fire prevention message (Home Office)

Specialist fire prevention officers spend much time checking plans of new and existing buildings to ensure compliance with codes of practice and building regulations. Here an architect is discussing a problem at a dry riser inlet box of a multi-storey high rise office block. In event of fire, this fire service connection would be quickly charged with water by one of the first crews and thus provide fire-fighting water at every floor level throughout the building (Devon Fire and Rescue Service)

TODAY'S REALITY

A large fire, in insurance terms, is one where the directly measurable fire damage is in excess of £50,000. In 1986 there were 981 such large fires in the United Kingdom. The Fire Protection Association carried out a detailed analysis of these large fires of 1986, and this revealed that of the 981 fires, 53 cost in excess of £1 million each. Over 60% of all fires started at night – the most dangerous period being between 9pm and 3am.

The three leading causes of large fires in 1986 were:
1. Deliberate ignition – causing more than £103 million worth of damage.
2. Misuse of electrical appliances and electrical installations, costing an estimated £55 million.
3. Smokers' materials (carelessly discarded cigarette ends and matches) – costing over £16 million.

Insurers and Lloyd's, underlining the commitment of UK insurers to the maintenance of sound technical standards and the reduction of property loss.

Three organizations have provided the foundation upon which the LPC is built:

Fire Offices' Committee
Fire Insurers' Research and Testing Organization
Fire Protection Association

The LPC brings under one umbrella seven loss prevention services:

Codes/standards	Information
Approvals/certification	Testing
Research	Advice
Training	

The Fire Protection Association (FPA) is the national fire-safety organization of the UK and one of twenty similar organizations worldwide. Its role is to identify and draw attention to fire dangers and to provide information and advice on all aspects of fire safety. Its services are specifically designed to assist the fire and security professionals in industry, commerce and the public sector as well as their professional advisers – insurance surveyors, fire-prevention officers, architects and consultants.

One of the most successful initiatives taken by the

FPA in conjunction with the Chief and Assistant Chief Fire Officers Association has been the organisation of the annual youth fire-prevention quiz. Now in its second decade, this annually involves tens of thousands of schoolchildren in its various knock-out rounds leading up to the finals, held in November each year during National Fire Safety week. Hopefully, a new generation of fire-safety-aware parents will grow from this novel and popular competition.

The probability of reducing fire deaths, injuries and property losses must, of course, relate to the work put in collectively on fire-prevention education in its various forms, both by the fire service and other supportive organisations. But firemen are fatalistic to a degree, for theirs is the sharp-end fire-fighting and rescue role, and their task is the recovery of bodies both young and old from fire and smoke-blackened premises and dwellings.

Firemen become regular witnesses of human fire tragedy and misfortune caused by neglect or sheer foolhardiness. Occasionally they are present at the aftermath of some classic folly such as the do-it-yourself enthusiast who actually smoked and dropped hot ash whilst using vast quantities of flammable floor-tile adhesive. Similarly, the elderly couple who, feeling cold in bed, placed a lighted paraffin lamp underneath their bed, little expecting such rapid results. And what of the dangerously obsolete wiring circuit in an old London property where the occupier, fed up with repeatedly blowing fuses, had replaced them with safety pins. Before long, he had unwittingly converted all the wiring in the house into a vast electric-fire element. Each of these three recent examples turned into a '999' call to the fire brigade, and firemen quickly braved dangerous conditions to save life and to prevent further damage to property by fire and smoke, just as their Victorian and Edwardian forebears had done on hundreds of occasions.

SURVIVAL

If fire occurs –
Close the door of the room where the fire is. This will help delay the spread of fire and smoke.
If a closed door feels warm, don't open it – the fire could be behind it.
Get everyone out. If you live in a flat do not use the lift.
'Phone the fire brigade by dialling '999' from a neighbour's home or a 'phone box. State clearly where the fire is.

If you are cut off by fire –
Remember that smoke is as deadly as flames. Close the door and any other openings and block the gaps with bedding or other material.
Go to the window, try to attract attention and wait for the fire brigade.
If the room becomes smoky, stay low – it's easier to breathe at floor level.
Think about making your escape.
If the window is jammed, break it. Try and remove jagged glass from the lower sill and cover it with a blanket.
Drop cushions or bedding to break your fall.
Get out feet first and lower yourself to the full length of your arms before dropping.

Welephant – the national fire safety mascot of the British Fire Service. Created by a teenager in Manchester in the late seventies, Welephant has now been adopted as a popular feature of the fire safety message to children particularly in school presentations up and down the country (Devon Fire and Rescue Service)

LIGHTNING NEVER STRIKES TWICE?

On 24 June 1983, a massive fire in the Ministry of Defence's Donnington Military Warehouse complex near Telford, in Shropshire, resulted in damaged estimated at £165 million. Despite a thorough investigation by fire service and police forensic specialists, the cause was finally recorded as 'unknown'. An inquiry recommended more stringent fire precautions and many of these were subsequently implemented.

But disaster was to strike again at Donnington. On 25 April 1988, a second huge conflagration took hold of another large warehouse full of transport spares for the British Army. Twenty pumps and over one hundred firemen battled for hours to contain the fire and prevent it from spreading to other warehouses nearby.

As in 1983, the warehouse was a total loss, although the fire was successfully contained to the one building. The estimated loss from the 'second' Donnington blaze is put at over £100 million, and the cause is still under investigation.

But, unlike the community of the turn of the century, today's public at large has a wealth of opportunity through the affluent trappings of the modern age to be careless and neglectful towards fire safety. Perhaps the day will arrive when fire deaths, injuries and losses will show a diminishing trend and give some respite to the fire-fighters, be they serving in a large city or in a rural shire. Such a Utopian respite will have been well earned.

EPILOGUE

When I first joined the fire service over twenty-five years ago, my sights were set on a career which would offer a personal challenge, excitement and something of the unexpected. The past two decades and more have certainly never been dull and in every respect have been years that I would happily relive, given the chance.

Job satisfaction came very early during my first week as an operational fireman, raw from training school after the three-month basic recruits' course. As part of a crew, I helped to care for and free a seriously injured lorry driver trapped for an hour in his crushed cab after he had crashed into the front of a terraced house. He survived the ordeal, and so too did I. As recruits, we were well prepared during training for the human suffering of which firemen are part, and the message was hammered into us: 'Although you will get used to the occasional awful sights at fires and accidents, remember it's a different set of people every time and your primary role as a fireman is to be the provider of comfort and assistance as well as a rescuer.'

Despite the thorough recruits' course, however, and regular on-station training, my real operational learning came during subsequent '999' calls where every incident, whether fire, road crash or leakage of dangerous chemicals, demanded a different approach. Here in fact lies the real strength of a fire-fighter's skill – his ability to act as part of a closely co-ordinated team or as a quick-

Firemen and the foe (London Fire Brigade)

FOR BRAVERY

'It is with pride and pleasure that this month we use the space normally occupied by our editorial to record the awards of two George Medals, three British Empire Medals and a Commendation to members of the Glasgow Fire Brigade for heroism during the disastrous whisky warehouse fire.

'We are sure that these awards will be a tribute not only to the men concerned but also to the whole of the Glasgow Fire Brigade, to the memory of the nineteen who died, and indeed to the hazardous work carried out by fire-fighters every day throughout the country.'

From *The Fire Journal*, November 1960 issue

thinking individual. These skills are put to the test especially when people are at risk; when, as is often the case, seconds can cost lives. Indeed, bearing in mind that a newly posted fireman can be as young as eighteen years of age, there can be few other professions where young recruits are so quickly put into the front line ready and likely to win their spurs at any moment. And for those with rank responsibilities, command and leadership qualities are also of paramount importance.

As an example, in 1972 during a time when I commanded a busy two-pump London Fire Brigade station at Islington, we turned out to a '999' road crash call outside Essex Road underground station during the morning rush hour. After some five hectic minutes wriggling through the traffic, the two pumps arrived at the accident site and we found a chaotic scene awaiting us.

A 32 ton (tonne) articulated lorry loaded with four large new tractors had collided with a moped at a traffic-light junction. The moped had gone under the lorry trailer and, as the lorry driver braked fiercely, the moped had caught fire. Its rider lay fatally injured in the road. But that was not all. The fire underneath the lorry trailer had developed rapidly and by the time my two pumps, crewed by eight firemen, were at the scene, the flames had engulfed the tractors and had spread into a nearby newsagent's canopy and shopfront, trapping about eight people inside. The lorry driver was also bleeding profusely from a serious head wound and was naturally in a state of shock. The only other valuable uniformed assistance at the scene was a police constable. Yet every one of my firemen knew their priorities, as one of the two crews attacked the shopfront fire whilst the others dealt with the dying and injured casualties. Within about eight minutes, the scene was under some semblance of calm control.

A larger incident that illustrates just how young and inexperienced firemen play their part during major rescue situations occurred at the fateful Worsley Hotel fire of Friday 13 December 1974 in Clifton Gardens, Maida Vale, London. As already described, over thirty residents were trapped on upper floors and ledges by the smoke from two separate fires, yet firemen climbed up to and rescued every one of those trapped, using ladders of all types, despite fire breaking out along the entire hotel frontage imperilling rescuers and rescued alike.

Of the courageous rescue team, six firemen under my command had less than eight months' service, whilst for one it was his very first night duty and only his fifth '999' call of that shift. Sadly, about an hour later, one of those probationers fresh from his ladder rescue success was killed when part of the roof of the hotel suddenly fell in, ironically whilst fire-fighters were bringing the fire under control. The Worsley fire surely epitomised in those few dramatic hours most aspects of a fireman's calling: the drama and danger, the exhilaration of a rescue safely carried out, and the ultimate sacrifice made.

However, despite the tragedy of such incidents as the Worsley Hotel, many emergency calls have a lighter side, humour often encouraged by firemen themselves in order to support the morale and spirit of a victim caught up in one of the tens of thousands of human dilemmas responded to by the fire service each year. Fire-fighters learn to develop a very special sense of the funny side of life, for without it they would probably not survive some parts of casualty work at its most unpleasant. Humour and the ability to laugh at oneself also help to build the tremendous esprit de corps and camaraderie that imbue firemen everywhere.

That the community at large appreciates its public fire service is hopefully beyond doubt, but life in the 1980s does bring its difficulties to fire crews, apart from the ever-spiralling fire losses and increased genuine '999' calls. Arson is a growing and worrying feature and shows no sign of diminishing. Today, urban vandalism leads to damage to street fire hydrants and fixed fire-fighting installations in buildings, as well as an increasing number of malicious '999' false alarm calls.

The future may be unknown but one thing is certain – despite much technological progress with fire-engines and fire-fighting equipment over the past 150 years and particularly during the last two decades, there is no likelihood of there being a ready substitute for the human fire-fighter. Today, the men and women of the modern fire service carry the mantle of their forbears of Roman times, of the insurance company years, of the harsh disciplines of the Massey Shaw era, and of those whose courage and endurance helped them to survive the horrors of the London blitz.

Images of the modern fire service and its dangerous work will surely continue to appear on television screens and across newspaper columns almost daily. As the nation's premier emergency and rescue organisation this is only right and proper. Hopefully these images will continue to remind the world at large of the value, efficiency and bravery of its fire service and its fire-fighters as they regularly and selflessly confront one of the most primeval and persistent enemies of mankind – fire.

(Overleaf) *A young life is saved. During the early stages of a fire in a second floor flat, a mother dropped her two young children to neighbours below before jumping herself. Sadly, she died from her injuries but here a leading fireman gently cradles one of the two children to a waiting ambulance. Despite some serious burns, both children survived. Allerton, Bradford, West Yorkshire. 22 September 1987* (West Yorkshire Fire Service)

CHRONOLOGICAL INDEX OF SIGNIFICANT BRITISH FIRES OF THE PAST 150 YEARS

Date	Place	Result
16 Oct 1834	Palace of Westminster	Both Houses of Parliament destroyed but Westminster Hall saved.
10 Jan 1838	Royal Exchange, City of London	Second Royal Exchange building on same site to be destroyed by fire.
30 Oct 1841	The Armoury, Tower of London	Collection of militaria back to James II lost.
19 Aug 1843	Toppings Wharf, London	Church and riverside warehouses.
19 March 1853	Windsor Castle	Prince of Wales Tower damaged.
6 Oct 1854	Hillgate, Gateshead	Wool and oil warehouse.
22 June 1861	Tooley Street, London	11 acres (4.4ha) of riverside warehouses lost; £2 million damage; James Braidwood killed.
3 Sept 1872	Canterbury Cathedral	Plumber's blowtorch caused £3,000 fire damage.
7 Dec 1882	Alhambra Theatre, London	2 firemen killed.
8 Dec 1882	Wood Street, City of London	36 buildings destroyed; 1 fireman killed.
18 Feb 1885	Blackburn, Lancs	Cotton mill; 2 firemen killed.
3 Feb 1886	Portland Street, Manchester	Warehouses; £100,000 damage.
18 Nov 1886	Hampton Court Palace apartments	15 different fire brigades attended; £20,000 damage.
10 Aug 1887	Whiteleys, Bayswater, London	Department store; 4 firemen killed; £500,000 loss.
5 Sept 1887	Theatre Royal, Exeter	188 lives lost.
1 Jan 1890	School, Forest Gate, London	26 pauper children perished.
26 June 1891	Leith, Scotland	Provision merchant's; 2 firemen killed.
22 Dec 1891	Tottenham Court Road, London	Department store; 25 steam pumps in use.

Date	Place	Result
9 Jan 1892	NER warehouse, Leeds	1 fireman killed.
5 Jan 1893	Juniper Street, Liverpool	Cotton warehouse; 2 firemen killed.
18 Nov 1894	Nottingham lace market	£150,000 damage.
16 Feb 1896	Church Street, Soho, London	Tenements; 9 residents killed.
29 July 1896	High Street, Ilfracombe, Devon	35 shops and houses; £100,000 loss.
12 Jan 1897	Purfleet, Essex	4,000 barrels petroleum involved.
25 April 1898	Dunlop Street, Glasgow	Warehouses; 100 firemen at work.
12 May 1899	Chemical works, St Helens	Fire and explosion; 5 workers killed.
5 June 1899	Hadfield, Derbyshire	Cotton mill; 1,000 workers laid off.
25 Sept 1900	Warboys village, Cambs	50 people homeless; 1 fireman killed; cause, children playing with matches.
5 Oct 1900	Welbeck Abbey, Notts	£100,000 damage; residence of Duke of Portland.
14 Jan 1901	Hat factory, Denton, Manchester	Fire and explosion; 13 workers killed.
23 Dec 1901	Liverpool Overhead Railway	6 passengers killed.
9 June 1902	Queen Victoria Street, City of London	10 office workers perished.
27 Jan 1903	Colney Hatch Asylum, Herts	51 patients dead.
1 June 1903	Eton College	2 pupils killed.
10 Dec 1903	Sandringham	Small fire in bedroom; queen in residence.
19 Nov 1905	Lodging house, Watson Street, Glasgow	39 dead – 368 had been sleeping on 5 floors.
14 June 1906	ss *Haverford*, Huskisson Dock, Liverpool	Explosion and fire; 10 dead.
7 Sept 1907	Newmarket Town Hall	3 dead during cinema show.
1 Nov 1908	Bute Street, Cardiff	Flour mill; explosion and fire.
20 April 1909	Whisky bond, Belfast	£160,000 damage.

Date	Place	Result
12 Sept 1910	GWR Millbay Docks, Plymouth	Crowd restrained by Royal Marines.
24 Dec 1910	Hawes Junction, Midland Railway	2 trains in collision; severe fire; 9 dead.
27 Feb 1911	Bankside, London	Paper and rag warehouse; 2 firemen killed.
3 Nov 1912	John Barker, Kensington, London	Department store; 5 shop girls killed.
11 June 1913	Paper mills, Barnsley	£50,000 loss; 250 workers idle.
19 Sept 1914	Canning Town, east London	Confectionery factory; 2 females dead, 3 firemen badly injured.
22 May 1915	Quintinshill, Caledonian Railway	Trains in collision, then severe fire; 215 soldiers, 10 civilians killed.

World War I saw fires caused by aerial bombardment.
These raids on the East Coast, London and the South
East took place between 31 May 1915 and 28 May 1918.

Date	Place	Result
7 April 1916	Garrick Theatre, Hereford	6 girls killed.
15 June 1916	Rotherhithe Street, London	Riverside warehouses and contents burned for 51 days before put out.
19 Jan 1917	Silvertown, east London	Explosion and fire at munitions factory; 69 dead, 400 injured.
30 Jan 1918	Albert Embankment, London	Cattle-food warehouse; 7 firemen killed; future site of LFB HQ (1937)
10 June 1919	Trafford Park, Manchester	Oil warehouses; £300,000 loss.
21 April 1921	Skelton's spade and shovel factory, Sheffield	£100,000 loss.
8 Aug 1921	Stratford, east London	Timber yard; £1 million loss.
4 Jan 1922	Timber yard, Cleveland Road, Hartlepool	Fire damage spread to 51 houses and 40 acres (16ha) of adjacent timber stacks; cause, spark from steam locomotive.
11 April 1923	East London	Tobacco warehouse; £850,000 loss.

Date	Place	Result
21 April 1924	Power house, Great Ferndale Collieries, Rhondda Fach	£300,000 damage.
26 Oct 1924	Film factory, Wardour Street, London	£1 million loss.
10 March 1925	Madame Tussaud's, Baker Street, London	Waxworks; £200,000 damage.
17 Oct 1925	Southampton Docks	Sugar warehouse; £300,000 loss.
23 Feb 1926	Custom House, Cardiff	Many businesses affected; £400,000 damage.
26 Feb 1926	Oulton Hall, Tarporley, Cheshire	6 fatalities; £200,000 loss.
7 July 1927	Otley, Oldham	Printing works; £200,000 damage.
6 Oct 1928	Chiswick, Middlesex	Wallpaper manufacturer's; £500,000 loss.
11 Aug 1929	St Andrews Dock, Hull	Landing stage, 7 new trawlers, offices, 150 railway vans damaged by fire; £300,000 loss.
9 Sept 1930	Riverside warehouses, Wapping, London	Contents included cocoa beans, butter and rubber; £600,000 loss.
18 Nov 1931	Luxury liner *Furness Withy*, 20,000 tons, dry dock, Belfast.	Fire damage £1 million whilst undergoing refit after earlier fire (17 June 1931) in Bermuda.
3 April 1933	Bonded warehouse, West India Dock, East London	1 million gal (220,000 litres) of rum lost, value £350,000.
25 Sept 1935	Colonial Wharf, Wapping, London	Warehouses containing tea and wine; £500,000 loss.
12 Feb 1936	Film studios, Elstree	£500,000 damage.
30 Nov 1936	Crystal Palace, Anerley Hill, south London	Paxton's historic building of 1851 totally destroyed except for two towers.
19 May 1937	LMS goods depot, Lawley Street, Birmingham	£400,000 loss.

Date	Place	Result
7 Feb 1938	Witton, Birmingham	Car electrics manufacturers; £550,000 damage.

World War II brought action to the home front; many fires were caused by incendiary and high explosive raids, V1 flying bombs and V2 rockets. Enemy action started on 9 May 1940 and ended on 27 March 1945.

Three of the most concentrated raids were on Coventry on 14 November 1940, the City of London on 29 December 1940 and Greater London on 10 May 1941. The lengthiest continuous raiding was on London and its suburbs for 57 consecutive nights from 7 September to 3 November 1940.

Date	Place	Result
11 April 1946	Kirby, Liverpool	Cotton warehouse; £520,000 loss.
8 Aug 1947	Spondon, Derbyshire	Rayon factory; £500,000 damage.
22 April 1949	NCB, West Hartlepool	Pit-prop store; £600,000 loss.
7 Nov 1949	Gladstone Dock, Liverpool	Wool, rubber and motor vehicle warehouse; £2 million loss.
23 Nov 1950	Treorchy, Glamorgan	Electrical engineer's; £750,000 loss.
24 Nov 1951	Ashley Road, Bristol	Explosion and fire at petrol station; 11 dead; likely cause – spark in electrical apparatus.
21 Dec 1951	BR goods warehouse, Eldon Street, London	£1 million loss; 3 firemen killed, 12 seriously injured; 200 pumps and 500 firemen at scene.
13 June 1952	Cotton mill, Rochdale	£1 million loss.
28 July 1953	Newport, Monmouth	Cardboard manufacturer; £750,000 damage.
3 Feb 1954	Ind Coope & Allsop, Burton-on-Trent	Hop warehouses; £850,000 loss.
10 March 1955	Halford Cycle Co, Birmingham	Warehouse and shops; £1 million loss.
23 Feb 1956	Eastwood Mills, Keighley, West Riding	8 employees killed; cause, careless use of blow lamp.
12 Feb 1957	Jaguar car factory, Coventry	£4 million loss.
4 April 1957	Wolverhampton	Tyre manufacturers; £1 million damage.
11 May 1957	Glasgow	Corn mill and store; £1¼ million loss.

Date	Place	Result
23 Jan 1958	Smithfield Meat Market, London	2 firemen dead; 40 hours before under control; 390 pumps and 1,700 firemen attended.
7 April 1959	Harrison Gibsons, Ilford, Essex	Department store; £1 million loss.
6 July 1959	Rolls-Royce, Mountsorrel, Leicester	Car manufacturers; £3 million loss.
28 March 1960	Cheapside Street, Glasgow	Whisky bond; 14 firemen, 5 salvage men killed; £5 million loss.
22 June 1960	Hendersons department store, Liverpool	11 dead; £1 million damage.
1 May 1961	Top Storey Club, Bolton, Lancs	19 fatalities
4 May 1962	Morris Commercial Motor Works, Bordesley, Birmingham	£2½ million loss.
17 Jan 1963	Croydon, Surrey	Tenement; 6 children killed; cause, paraffin heater knocked over.
17 July 1963	Department store, Sauchiehall Street, Glasgow	1 shopworker dead, 9 rescued by firemen.
7 Dec 1963	New BEA Air Terminal, Cromwell Road, west London	£5 million loss; 30 pumps and 8 turntable ladders in use.
1 April 1964	Bedford Hotel, Brighton	3 residents killed.
12 Nov 1964	ss *Pyrrhus*, West Huskinsson Dock, Liverpool	Mixed cargo involved; 22 hours of fire-fighting.
15 Sept 1965	Esso refinery, Fawley, Hants	4 firemen injured; 37 pumps in use.
22 Sept 1965	Grocers' Hall, City of London	Livery hall (which survived 1940–41 blitz); 55 appliances, 300 firemen involved.
18 Dec 1965	Motor industry plastics factory, Birmingham	£1½ million loss.

Date	Place	Result
16 Feb 1966	RAF station, Neatishead, Norfolk	Underground stores; 2 firemen killed.
30 Aug 1966	Dwelling, Glasgow	7 tenants dead.
8 Sept 1966	Paper-reel factory, Rochdale	£1 million damage.
14 April 1967	Ironmonger's store, Leeds	18 rescued by firemen.
22 Oct 1967	Dwelling, Wallasey, Cheshire	1 adult, 7 children killed.
22 Oct 1967	Kelloggs, Stretford, Lancs	47 pumps from 11 brigades; 9 firemen injured.
19 Feb 1968	Harrison Gibsons, Bromley	Department store; 25 pumps, 3 turntable ladders.
26 Feb 1968	Old persons' home, Shelton, Shropshire	24 female residents killed.
18 Nov 1968	James Watt Street, Glasgow	Upholstery factory; 22 workers dead.
6 June 1969	Leinster Towers Hotel, Bayswater, London	50 residents rescued by firemen; 30 pumps.
17 July 1969	Dudgeons Wharf, Millwall, east London	Explosion in derelict tank farm; 5 firemen and 1 civilian killed.
26 Dec 1969	Rose and Crown Hotel, Saffron Walden, Essex	11 residents dead; likely cause, TV set left switched on.
23 May 1970	Menai railway bridge, Caernarvon-shire, N Wales	£2 million damage.
23 Oct 1970	MV *Pacific Glory* off Portsmouth	Major fire on tanker.
22 Dec 1970	Hotel, Redcar	4 residents killed, 16 rescued.
24 Dec 1970	Wolfrun Centre, Wolver-hampton	Fire in 11 acre (4.4ha) covered shopping mall; extensive smoke damage.
6 May 1971	Woolworth's warehouse, Rochdale	£4½ million loss.

Date	Place	Result
9 Aug 1971	Battle Bridge Lane, Tooley Street, London	50 pumps, 300 firemen; 3 firemen badly burnt.
5 July 1972	Coldharbour Hospital, Sherborne, Dorset	30 mentally handicapped patients dead.
25 Aug 1972	Cash-and-carry warehouse, Kilburnie Street, Glasgow	7 firemen killed.
18 Nov 1972	Maryhill Road, Glasgow	Shops/offices and tenements; 1 fireman and 1 civilian dead; 5 firemen injured.
3 July 1973	Courtaulds, Preston, Lancs	Rayon factory; £4 million loss.
24 July 1973	Esplanade Hotel, Oban	10 residents dead.
3 Aug 1973	Summerland pleasure centre, Douglas, Isle of Man	49 fatalities.
5 Oct 1973	MV *Barrad Crest* off Plymouth, Devon	10 firemen injured in explosion whilst fire-fighting on board.
1 June 1974	Nypro UK, Flixborough, South Humberside	Explosion and fire in chemical works; 28 dead and 100 injured; £36 million damage.
17 June 1974	Westminster Hall, Palace of Westminster, London	Terrorist fire bomb; damage confined to roof.
13 Dec 1974	Worsley Hotel, Maida Vale, London	6 residents dead, 32 rescued; 1 fireman killed, 3 others seriously burnt; cause, arson.
15 Dec 1974	Fairfield Old Persons' Home, Edwalton, Notts	18 residents dead.
1 Aug 1975	Chrysler Motors, Coventry	£7 million loss; 150 firemen involved.
22 Nov 1975	Cold storage depot, Walsall	£8 million damage.
6 Jan 1976	Flatlets, seafront, Brighton	4 residents killed.

Date	Place	Result
29 April 1976	Newcastle and Gateshead Rapid Transit Metro	Fire and explosion in pressurised underground workings; 11 workmen rescued.
11 Sept 1976	Westoning, Beds	Fully laden petrol tanker overturned and ignited, centre of village; 3 shops, 6 dwellings destroyed; no serious casualties.
5 Jan 1977	Wensley Lodge Old Persons' Home, Hessle, N Humberside	11 residents dead.
20 Jan 1977	Offices, Manchester	7 female workers killed.
27 March 1977	Restaurant and flats, Dover, Kent	6 residents, 1 fireman dead.
25 Sept 1977	St John's Centre, Liverpool	Covered three-level shopping complex; extensive smoke and heat damage.
6 July 1978	BR, Taunton, Somerset	Sleeper train; 12 passengers killed; likely cause, bags of linen stored against heaters.
26 Sept 1978	HMS *Glasgow*, Swan Hunter Yard, Tyne and Wear	Fire in lower decks; 8 shipyard workers dead.
1 Oct 1978	Midland Railway warehouse, Camden Town, London	1 fireman killed; 35 pumps; £5 million loss.
4 March 1979	Bedford School, Bedford	Sixteenth-century public school.
8 May 1979	Woolworths, Piccadilly, Manchester	10 dead; polyurethane foam-filled furniture involved.
20 May 1979	Dwelling, Sutton Coldfield, West Midlands	6 killed.
17 Dec 1979	St John's Centre, Liverpool	£12 million loss; *see also* fire of 25 September 1977.
27 Jan 1980	British Aerospace, Weybridge, Surrey	Aircraft spares warehouse; £27½ million loss.
18 March 1980	Hostel, Kilburn, London	9 fatalities.

Date	Place	Result
10 July 1980	Alexandra Palace, north London	£31 million loss; 200 firemen involved.
16 Aug 1980	Denmark Place, Soho, London	Unlicensed drinking club; 37 persons unable to escape and perished.
26 Feb 1981	Post Office stores, Saltley, Birmingham	£10 million damage.
2 May 1981	George Hotel, Reading	Sixteenth-century building; 3 residents dead, 13 rescued.

From 5–13 July 1981, civil disturbances took place at Toxteth in Liverpool, Moss Side in Manchester and in Handsworth in West Midlands. Firemen from the 3 brigades involved dealt with over 70 separate arson fires, including one attack on a fire station; 7 fire engines were damaged and 3 fire-fighters injured.

Date	Place	Result
6 Sept 1981	Chemical works, Stalybridge, Greater Manchester	1 civilian killed; 37 pumps; 200 firemen.
6 March 1982	Discothèque, Rye, E Sussex	2 teenagers dead.
12 Aug 1982	London Transport, between Wood Green and Bounds Green stations	2 underground trains, in tunnel; 350 passengers led to safety by firemen.
23 Sept 1982	Chemical works, Salford, Greater Manchester	£1½ million loss after fire and explosion.
24 June 1983	Ministry of Defence stores, Donnington, Shropshire	£165 million loss – record UK sum to date.
30 Aug 1983	Amoco Refinery, Milford Haven, Dyfed	44 pumps (30 from Dyfed FB) involved; 60 hours of fire-fighting saved refinery.
1 Sept 1983	Candar Hotel, Ilfracombe, Devon	Extensive fire spread into narrow streets adjacent; Water pumped from sea.
6 Nov 1983	Unregistered factory, Gravesend, Kent	Fire and explosion killed 7 persons, all from one family.
14 Jan 1984	Maysfield Leisure Centre, Belfast	6 fatalities.

Date	Place	Result
9 July 1984	York Minster	South transept and roof damaged after lightning strike.
11 May 1985	Bradford City football club, Valley Parade, Bradford	56 spectators killed; cause believed to be carelessly disposed cigarette.
22 Aug 1985	British Airtours' Boeing 737, Manchester International Airport	55 passengers dead.
28 Jan 1986	MV *Ebn Magid* off Portland, Dorset	8,000 fire-fighting man hours.
31 March 1986	Hampton Court Palace, Middlesex	1 resident dead.
22 March 1987	BP refinery, Grangemouth	1 worker killed; 200 firemen involved.
18 Nov 1987	London Transport, Kings Cross station	30 passengers and 1 fireman killed.
1 Jan 1988	Dwelling, Merthyr Tydfil, Mid Glamorgan	Father and 4 children dead.
25 April 1988	Ministry of Defence stores, Donington, Shropshire	Second major fire and loss on same site, *see* 24 June 1983.
6 July 1988	*Piper Alpha* oil production platform	167 workers dead.
22 Sept 1988	*Ocean Odyssey* oil drilling rig	1 worker killed, 66 rescued.
19 Dec 1988	House of Fraser department store, Plymouth, Devon	150 firemen involved in six hour battle to prevent fire spreading into other stores nearby. £22 million loss. Likely cause, arson.
8 Jan 1989	British Midland Boeing 737, M1 Motorway, Kegworth, Leicestershire	47 killed, 79 survivors after fire in engine.

BIBLIOGRAPHY

Austin, Tony. *Aberfan: the Story of a Disaster* (Hutchinson, 1967)

Ballantyne, R. M. *Fighting the Flames* (Thomas Nelson, 1867)

Blackstone, G. V. *A History of the British Fire Service* (Routledge & Kegan Paul, 1957)

COI/Home Office. *Home Fire Safety Guide* (1987) and other fire-prevention booklets

Collier, Richard. *The City that Wouldn't Die* (Collins, 1959)

Fire (journal), various from 1908

Fire and Water (journal), various from 1890

Fire and Water – a National Fire Service Anthology (Lindsay Drummond, 1942)

Fire Directory, 1988/89 (FMJ International Publications Ltd)

Firebrace, Sir Aylmer. *Fire Service Memories* (Andrew Melrose, 1948)

Fireman, The (journal), various from 1884

HMSO *Annual Reports of Her Majesty's Chief Inspectors of Fire Services for England and Wales, and Scotland*

HMSO *Front Line* (1942)

HMSO *Manuals of Firemanship* (various)

HMSO *Report of the Joint Committee on Standards of Fire Cover* (1985)

HMSO *Review of Fire Policy* (1980)

Holloway, Sally. *London's Noble Fire Brigades* (Cassell, 1973)

Holloway, Sally. *Moorgate* (David & Charles, 1988)

Honeycombe, Gordon. *Red Watch* (Hutchinson, 1976)

Jackson, W. Eric. *London's Fire Brigades* (Longmans, 1966)

Morris, C.C.B. *Fire* (Blackie, 1939)

Nicholls, Arthur. *Going to Blazes* (Hale, 1978)

Richardson, M. L. *London's Burning* (Hale, 1941)

Rolt, L. T. C. *Red for Danger* (David & Charles, 1982)

Shaw, Eyre Massey. *A Complete Manual on the Working of the Fire Brigade of London* (C. & E. Layton, 1876)

UK Fire Brigades, various annual reports together with their periodic journals and magazines

Wallington, Neil. *Fireman! A Personal Account* (David & Charles, 1979)

Wallington, Neil. *Firemen at War* (David & Charles, 1982)

Wallington, Neil. *'999' – The Accident and Crash Rescue Work of the Fire Service* (David & Charles, 1987)

Wassey, M. *Ordeal by Fire.* (Secker & Warburg, 1941)

While, Jack. *50 years of Fire Fighting in London* (Hutchinson, 1931)

INDEX